MW00611093
VETERANS ADMINISTRATION HOSPITAL
FALK SCHOOL
ALUMNI HALL
THAW HALL
STATE HALL
PARKMAN
AVENUE
AVE.
20TH CENTURY CLUB
PA. HIST. SOC.
BIGELOW BOULEVARD
PARKING
LYTTON
PARKING
SYRIA MOSQUE
PITTSBURGH ATHLETIC CLUB
MASONIC TEMPLE
TENNYSON
FACULTY PARKING
CLAPP HALL
RUSKIN APARTMENTS
WQED
HEINZ MEMORIAL CHAPEL
FIFTH AVENUE
AVE.
MELLON INSTITUTE
GRADUATE HALL
Y.M.H.A.

All profits from this book will be donated to
The Thomas Detre Chair in Geriatric Medicine.

ISBN: 978-1-4349-0283-2
Library of Congress Control Number: 2008934854

Printed in the United States of America
First Printing

For information or to order additional books, please write:
Dorrance Publishing Co., Inc.
701 Smithfield St.
Third Floor
Pittsburgh, PA 15222
U.S.A.
1-800-788-7654
www.dorrancebookstore.com

Front endleaf: University of Pittsburgh, Oakland campus, ca. 1970
Back endleaf: University of Pittsburgh, Oakland campus, ca. 2005

A HISTORY OF UPMC

BEYOND THE BOUNDS

By Mary Brignano

Dorrance Publishing Co., Inc.
Pittsburgh, Pennsylvania 15222

AT HEART, IT IS JUST A SIMPLE STORY OF COMING OF AGE ... **AGAINST ENORMOUS RESISTANCE.**

— Jeffrey A. Romoff

Contents

Preface

When UPMC asked me to write a book about its history, I accepted the challenge with both enthusiasm and a few qualms. As a Pittsburgher and the author of more than thirty histories of Pittsburgh hospitals, foundations, companies, and organizations, I was eager to learn more about this global health enterprise that has transformed the economic landscape of western Pennsylvania. UPMC's rapid rise – juxtaposed against the decline of heavy manufacturing and the loss of major corporations – is a turning point in the history of my city.

But like many longtime Pittsburghers, I had a lot of questions about this "juggernaut" that had taken over the management of our historic hospitals. Who were these people? Can we trust them? How did they create UPMC? Why? What risks and hurdles had they overcome? What makes UPMC different from other health systems? What can UPMC's history teach other health systems, academic medical centers, and government officials who must deal with our nation's critically ailing health care system?

UPMC gave me free rein to look at the organization and its growth. With George A. Huber, then UPMC's corporate counsel, I interviewed more than sixty people both inside and outside the institution. Ideas for the narrative began to emerge from the time of my first meetings with Thomas Detre, MD, the Hungarian-born psychiatrist who first drove the ascent of UPMC, and Jeffrey A. Romoff, who followed Dr. Detre from Yale as a "trailing spouse" and became president of UPMC in 1992. Although both these protagonists are more interested in thinking about the future than about the past, I found them to be candid and charismatic as they discussed their motivations, philosophies, challenges, opponents, strategies, struggles, achievements, and occasional missteps. Mr. Romoff made it clear that UPMC's success had not come easily, and that the book should not back away from the conflicts in the organization's history.

What I took away from these conversations was an impression of people who are visionary, passionate, audacious, engaging, exceptionally intelligent, and principled – people with a commitment to improving health and the region in which they live. Early in the project I decided that the author should stand back and let Dr. Detre, Mr. Romoff, and their articulate colleagues tell UPMC's story with the immediacy of their own words. What has emerged is a sort of documentary in print.

I came to believe that the forceful personalities of Thomas Detre and Jeffrey A. Romoff drove the development of UPMC and its institutional culture – a culture that pushes relentlessly against what Romoff calls "the tyranny of the dominant paradigm." By this he means the prevailing system of beliefs that legitimize the status quo – regardless of that system's relevance or validity. Whether working to reduce wait time for patient appointments with physicians or to make radiology coverage available 24/7, Romoff is not one to accept "because it has always been done that way" as a valid reason for continuing an ineffective model. He, and UPMC, incessantly assess, challenge, and test the paradigms that define the boundaries of traditional practices in the world of academic medical centers.

It's an exciting culture to be around. It's forward-looking. Nobody at UPMC seems satisfied with what he or she or anyone else accomplished yesterday. "Everything we did was disruptive to the status quo," Romoff said in one of our first meetings. "But the status quo, at least in my experience, is always inadequate," he added. "And worse than inadequate in health care, it's also harmful."

The remark offers an insight into the drive for excellence that I believe motivated Detre and Romoff. Local attempts to portray these two as "empire builders" misses the point. Certainly they created a huge, centrally managed enterprise. But size was not the goal. Quality was. Size was a means to the end. Their objective was to build and preserve an outstanding academic medical center that would provide world-class health care, generate large amounts of research funding for the University of Pittsburgh, and develop new products, businesses, and jobs for western Pennsylvania. To do good, UPMC had to be big.

The book's title, *Beyond the Bounds*, surfaced early into the project. I began to understand that a major theme in UPMC's history is advancing across barriers, breaking down walls that separate people and ideas, toppling whatever conventional wisdom blocks innovation. Nothing gets you in trouble faster at UPMC than saying, "But we've always done it this way."

Innovation is a creed at UPMC. Learning about Dr. Detre's life as a psychiatrist, I discovered that he was an innovator in advancing the care of patients by going beyond the bounds of psychiatry's turf to collaborate with other medical, scientific, and academic disciplines. I realized that UPMC's founders innovated too by applying an interdisciplinary, beyond-the-bounds approach to hospital administration. UPMC brought matrix management to health care operations, drawing together people from various disciplines to improve clinical care and administration. Jeffrey A. Romoff, a former musician, turns to the metaphor of the orchestra to describe what he believes "UPMC has done brilliantly – to inspire people and institutions to collaborate, to leave their solo world and combine into something that is greater than each of the players individually."

"If there's a kind of cornerstone to American commerce, it is health care."

— G. Nicholas Beckwith III

Some biologists believe that in the evolution of both human economies and natural ecosystems, competition for resources can drive innovation and increase productivity, diversity, and intensity of competition. What I learned in writing this book is that UPMC has created an entrepreneurial culture with the ability to compete, innovate, and harmonize disparate pieces. The organization has succeeded despite powerful antagonists and a harsh economic environment. Realizing that crisis can equal opportunity, it has recognized that the time to change, grow, and be successful is often when the ecology seems most inhospitable. Few if any academic medical centers – which have tended to be tradition-bound and slow to change – have demonstrated UPMC's managerial agility or boldness.

The Pittsburgh of the past made steel for the railroads and bridges that united a continent. As I see it, UPMC now manufactures and leverages ideas that will change how an electronically connected world may live and work tomorrow. "More innovation either occurs in health care or is spun out of health care or is some way collaborative with health care than any other industry," says G. Nicholas Beckwith III, UPMC board chair. "At 16 percent of GDP, health care is the biggest business in America. So if there's a kind of cornerstone to American commerce, it is health care."

Now headquartered at the top of the U.S. Steel Tower in downtown Pittsburgh, UPMC is similar in some ways to the steel industry it has displaced. "Andrew Carnegie and others transformed iron making from an artisanal activity into an industrial activity," observes UPMC Vice Chair Mark J. Laskow, who also chairs the

board of the Carnegie Hero Fund. UPMC is effecting a similar transformation in health care, he adds. "The nineteenth-century industrialists were doing what no one had done before. No one had organized enterprises on this scale, employed people on this scale, tried to work in unison to produce a uniform product in an economic way on this scale. They made mistakes. UPMC has made mistakes and as it goes along will continue to. But that's inherent in breaking new ground."

"There are a lot of things going on here that are fascinating," sums up Nick Beckwith.

Producing this book has been for me an absorbing opportunity to see how health care is transforming a historic city and attracting bright, talented clinicians, scientists, and managers to our midst. These are people who could work and live anywhere in the world – but they choose to come to Pittsburgh and to UPMC. And from Pittsburgh, they are breaking beyond the bounds of today to create the health enterprise of the future, and to touch the lives of people around the world.

—Mary Brignano

Thomas Detre, MD (seated), and Jeffrey A. Romoff

"The unencumbered flow of knowledge, inventions, and gifted individuals across conventional academic and industrial boundaries is essential for success."

— Thomas Detre, MD

Milestones in the history of the University of Pittsburgh, medicine, and the life of Thomas Detre, MD

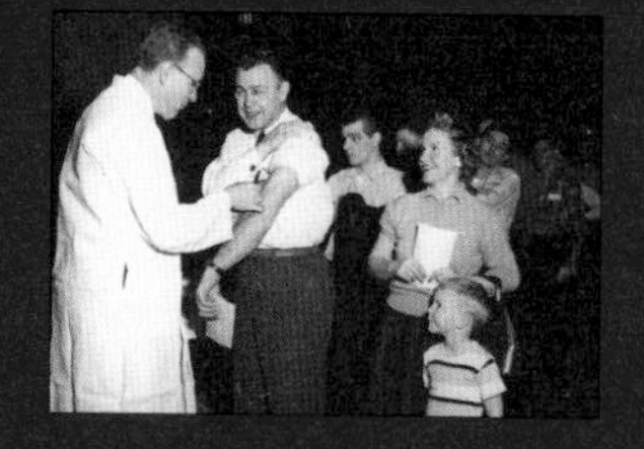
Administering polio vaccine, 1950s

1787–1970

1787 The University of Pittsburgh is founded.

1908 The University of Pittsburgh acquires the Western Pennsylvania Medical College, opened by Pittsburgh physicians in 1886.

1910 The Flexner Report, commissioned by the American Medical Association and the Carnegie Foundation for the Advancement of Teaching, calls for university-affiliated teaching hospitals with full-time faculty members and scientific research laboratories.

Early 1920s University of Pittsburgh Chancellor John G. Bowman promotes the dream of a great medical center.

1921–1922 The University of Pittsburgh buys land for a medical center. Over the next twenty years, various teaching hospitals will open here.

1924 Thomas Detre is born in Budapest, Hungary.

Western Psychiatric Institute and Clinic (WPIC)

1930 Creating the National Institutes of Health (NIH), Congress authorizes federally funded fellowships for research in basic biological and medical science.

1937 The forerunner of Blue Cross of Western Pennsylvania, a prepaid hospital insurance program, is established. The plan provides financial stability for hospitals and spurs demand for hospital beds.

1942 Western Psychiatric Institute and Clinic (WPIC) is formally dedicated.

1947 Thomas Detre escapes from Soviet-occupied Hungary to study and practice psychiatry in Rome.

NIH appropriations total $8,075,000.

1949 The Commonwealth of Pennsylvania transfers management of WPIC to the University of Pittsburgh.

The University of Pittsburgh receives major gifts from the Mellon and Scaife families to improve the quality of the School of Medicine and its faculty.

1950 Nationwide NIH appropriations rise to $52,714,000, including the first grants from the National Institute of Mental Health. NIH appropriations will continue to rise throughout the century, helping to put the United States at the forefront of medical research and development.

Early 1950s Antipsychotic drugs offer patients with schizophrenia and psychosis a chance to lead more normal and fulfilling lives.

1953 Dr. Detre immigrates to the United States; he joins the Department of Psychiatry at Yale University in 1955. Here he establishes a national reputation by joining psychiatry with biological, evidence-based medicine.

1955 The live polio vaccine, discovered at the University of Pittsburgh, comes into widespread use.

1960 Health care expenditures in the U.S. total $28 billion.

1965 Congress passes legislation creating Medicare and Medicaid.

The "University Health Center of Pittsburgh" (UHCP) is incorporated as an official coordinating body for the medical center. But it has no power over the independently governed and managed teaching hospitals.

1969 The Richard K. Mellon Charitable Trusts grant $5 million to the University of Pittsburgh to attract "an outstanding man as chairman" of the Department of Psychiatry.

1970 Health care expenditures in the U.S. rise to $75 billion.

I

Border Crossings

"First and foremost, I wanted to create a system which was focused on clinical and translational research, because academic medicine has a two-fold task. One is to advance knowledge, but the other is to study the available approaches to diagnosis and treatment, to provide optimal care with what we know today. You have to do the best you can do for your patients." — Thomas Detre, MD

Yet again, Thomas Detre confounded his colleagues at Yale University. On September 7, 1972, the forty-eight-year-old psychiatrist announced he was giving up his tenured full professorship for a new minefield of a job, far beyond the bounds of Ivy League prestige. The University of Pittsburgh School of Medicine had invited him to become chairman of the Department of Psychiatry and also director of the one hospital the university managed, Western Psychiatric Institute and Clinic (WPIC).

Thomas Detre, MD, the Hungarian-born psychiatrist who first drove the ascent of UPMC

Many Easterners thought of Pittsburgh as hopelessly provincial and its university as second-rate at best. Dr. Detre, however, intended to mine these supposedly unpromising resources to create a new health care model, "a center of excellence which would be focused on clinical research."

THOMAS DETRE: *This was the question my friends asked, why anybody in his right mind, much less the psychiatrist-in-chief at Yale-New Haven Hospital and a Hungarian-Jewish refugee besides, would leave Yale for any reason. But to move to Pittsburgh!? Even my family complained bitterly.*

"Nobody goes to Pittsburgh," the Easterners sniffed. "Planes don't even land there."

But Thomas Detre, around whose powerful leadership UPMC would eventually coalesce, predicted differently.

"Once we get there, the planes will land," he assured them in his velvety baritone. The central European accent turned the w's into v's, and courtly, old world manners only partly masked an iron will. Before long those planes did land, carrying talented young faculty and staff from Yale and other major universities, eager to follow their mentor on his quest to build "the most successful research-oriented department of psychiatry in the United States."

The Perils of Doing What You Think Is Right

Thomas Detre downplays his achievements, claiming that his strength lies in his "scouting" ability. He has spotted, recruited, inspired, and won the loyalty of immensely talented men and women. They have been drawn to his drive for excellence in medical care, his readiness to take risks, his intolerance of mediocrity, and his "unique talent for piercing taboos." They have delighted in his legendary charm and disarming self-deprecation. "I really don't take myself seriously, and I never did," Dr. Detre says. "I took my work seriously, but not myself." They were attracted to his compelling physical presence, emanating from dark, intense eyes and a stillness when listening that can suggest the image of a panther poised to spring. "A man of immense personal force," *The New York Times Magazine* described him in 1969.

Most of all, these recruits were thrilled by the freedom Detre offered – the freedom to unleash their ideas, break down walls between disciplines, and "bring down the tyranny of dominant paradigms" in order to advance science, education, and health.

Dr. Detre's friends have loved him for his wisdom, compassion, and many personal kindnesses over the years. A mentor to academic leaders around the country, he is often the first person people call when they need help or advice. "He is my

Jewish guardian angel," says J. Wray Connolly, the former senior vice president of H. J. Heinz Corporation who chaired the University of Pittsburgh's Board of Trustees from 1995 to 2001.

Detre puts it more analytically. "There are people who inspire confidence. I happen to be one of them. I cannot say that this is such a wonderful, special characteristic; I was born with it, and my father, who was a physician, had the same characteristic."

Plenty of other people, though, have resented, feared, distrusted, resisted, and fought him. A powerful, principled man who challenges the status quo and demands the highest levels of performance is bound to clash with people who do not feel that same fire in the belly to excel.

JEFFREY A. ROMOFF: *Doing what he thought was right is something that Tom did with great energy and vigor. Tom first and foremost believed in academic excellence. So every time he did anything that promoted academic excellence – taking resources from those who weren't producing and giving resources to those who were – he'd come up against enormous resistance.*

At every stage, at every *stage of anything interesting that was done here, there was always substantial resistance.*

Thomas Detre is less likely to be invigorated by the rhetoric of "the enemy," perhaps because he has experienced the reality of war. Over the years he learned how to win without actually stepping onto the battlefield himself. As Connolly puts it, "When Tom Detre wanted something, it happened. Even if no one agreed with him, it still happened."

THOMAS DETRE: *I think we all, including myself, don't like changes that involve "me." So I'm not surprised that they were not applauding loudly when I wanted to make changes. But between 1985 and 1995 the University of Pittsburgh School of Medicine was the fastest-growing research enterprise in the United States. So if you want to ask, "Was this strategy OK?" you could say, "Yes. It produced the expected results."*

Thomas Detre and his parents in Venice, mid-1930s

We [humans] are so constructed genetically that approximately 98 percent of us are obedient servants and about 2 percent of us or less are capable of independent thinking. OK? And whoever is domineering, we are willing to succumb and take it, and I think that's part of our animal nature.

I consider this very fortunate, because if everyone were like me, what the hell would we do?

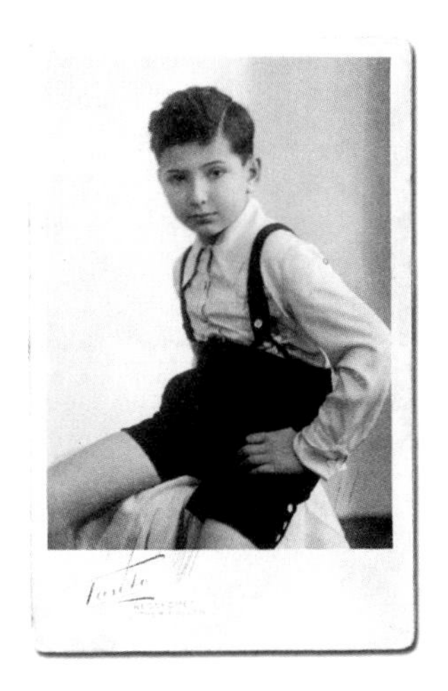

Thomas Detre seemed sure of himself, even as a boy.

Raised a Half-Century Ahead

Thomas Detre was born Tamás Feldmeier in Budapest in 1924, the only child of Géza Feldmeier, MD, a Berlin-trained obstetrician-gynecologist, and his wife, Gabriella Bauer. He grew up in the city of Kecskemét, his father's hometown, about eighty-five kilometers from the capital.

THOMAS DETRE: *My father was one of the best doctors I have ever known. His instinct for diagnosis was so acute that the public absolutely refused to consider him as only an obstetrician-gynecologist, although he had delivered nearly four thousand babies by the time he was deported to Auschwitz. My mother loved to dance, and drink, and play cards, and was absolutely outrageous in the best possible way. When my father was drafted during the First World War, she cut her hair, disguised herself in a soldier's uniform, and traveled by train to the Russian front, where he was stationed with the hussars. Because they were newly married, and she missed him.*

I was brought up very liberally. My parents were about half a century ahead of themselves in every respect.

His grandfather had made money and commercial history by exporting the region's abundant agricultural products all over Europe in refrigerated railroad cars.

THOMAS DETRE: *We went abroad every two years, religiously. It was a rare evening that my parents dined alone. And, like all intellectual middle-class children, I had Austrian and German frauleins [governesses]. So my first language was German, not Hungarian.*

My father's patients ranged from Catholic priests to actors to the king of the Gypsies. At Christmas, a whole Gypsy orchestra came in front of the house to serenade him.

Thomas Detre attended high school at Kecskemét's Gymnasium of Piarist Fathers (left). "Slightly stricter than the Jesuits," he deadpans.

Crossing the Line

After public grammar school, Tamás was educated at a private Catholic high school and college, the Gymnasium of Piarist Fathers – "slightly stricter than the Jesuits," he maintains. There, in a moment of appalling irony, he first became interested in psychiatry.

THOMAS DETRE: *Anti-Semitism in Hungary started to increase in the late 1930s and peaked in the early 1940s. You began hearing anti-Semitic remarks on the streets. One day, even at the Piarist gymnasium, a teacher of cultural history referred to Sigmund Freud as "the degenerate Jew who developed a pan-sexual view of human nature." I am actually grateful for that remark. It made me curious. I was only fourteen, but my father allowed me to read all his books about Freud. I decided that psychiatry was going to be an interesting discipline for me.*

My father was upset. He wanted me to be a "decent" doctor, not a psychiatrist.

Because no Jews were permitted to attend medical school, Tamás was forced to continue his education at the Academy of Law in Kecskemét. He also worked as a research assistant in the neuropsychiatric unit of Budapest's Jewish Hospital.

THOMAS DETRE: *The refugees arriving in Budapest told horror stories about what was going on in Nazi-occupied countries. I was convinced that our family had to get out of Europe. But my father was a highly decorated World War I officer. He said deportations would never happen in Hungary. He said his patients would protect him. I was more skeptical.*

When the Germans occupied Hungary in March 1944, I stayed in Kecskemét for a few days, but I saw it was not possible to remain safe in a small city. I packed some jewelry and went back to Budapest. That was the last time I saw my parents. The following year I learned they had died in Auschwitz along with twenty members of our family.

Alone in Budapest, the twenty-year-old student survived by his wits, by a fierce, grim pleasure in deceiving the enemy, and by luck. "This behavior characterized the survivors," he told an interviewer in 1998. Still, he said, survival "was largely random; the best people may not have survived, the nicest people may not have survived." He felt "a very profound sadness" not knowing his parents' whereabouts.

In Budapest, ordered to dig an air raid shelter under SS guard, he volunteered to treat an injured SS soldier. He then received a pass to move around the city as a physician. He later heard that many of his fellow workers had been executed. When the Nazis rounded up Jews on the streets, he pretended to be an engineer at work surveying the street, and the soldiers passed him by. He dug bodies out of bombed buildings. He spent three or four weeks locked up and guarded by Hungarian fascists – "gangsters," he called them – with machine guns.

Budapest, 1945, after the battles for the city during World War II

"Probably the most fearful, anxious moment of my life" came the day in November 1944 when he was taken to a collection place about ten kilometers from Budapest. Soldiers ordered people into two lines. In the first, longer line were those who were to be sent to concentration camps. In the second, much shorter line were those with a Schutzpass, a document created by Swedish diplomat Raoul Wallenberg. It proclaimed the bearer to be under the protection of the Swedish government. Tamás had no Schutzpass.

THOMAS DETRE: *Between the lines were the Hungarian fascists with machine guns so that nobody could cross the lines. I don't know, because I didn't have a watch, but it probably took me over an hour. I watched every one of them until I saw that everybody was looking somewhere else. And I crossed the four steps to the group that went back to Budapest.*

Experiences like this may have shaped what a student would call Detre's "knack for sweeping away the nonessentials."

Escape

Thomas Detre's identity card when he was a medical student

The Russian "liberation" of Hungary in 1945 enabled Detre to attend medical school at the Pázmány Péter University of Science in Budapest. Like many people who had lived through the Holocaust, he changed his German-sounding name. Those close to him suggested that he chose Detre because in French, *être* means "to be," and *d'être* is "for being."

His psychiatric studies crossed into new territory as well. His mentor, "a little known but very intelligent psychiatrist called Leopold Szondi," believed that psychoanalytic psychotherapy was ineffective in treating most biologically based mental disorders. Detre came to a lifelong conviction: For some illnesses, no amount of talking could make the patient better. "Psychotherapy alone is likely to be of major benefit only when the impairments originate exclusively in the sociopsychological roots and consequences of the illness," he would write in his definitive *Modern Psychiatric Treatment.*

By his early twenties the medical student had managed to become the acting director of a psychiatric hospital. In 1947 his sardonic refusal to leave the hospital to attend a May Day parade enraged the Communists. "If all the crazies are out marching," Detre had demanded, "who will take care of the crazies inside?"

The remark imperiled his freedom and his life. A former lover, now active in the Communist Party, warned him to leave Hungary as quickly as possible. "Darling," she said, "this is not the place for you. You have too big a mouth. Make every effort to get out." Through family connections he managed to get a visa to study at Rome University. He crossed into Italy in 1947.

THOMAS DETRE: *You've probably seen the movie* La Dolce Vita. *That was the period I lived in Rome – the late 1940s and early 1950s. I had a good time!*

In Rome he worked at Italy's National Research Council and also developed a lucrative private practice. One of his patients was the Pulitzer Prize-winning poet James Merrill, who would make Detre a pivotal figure in his memoir, *A Different Person.* Merrill vividly remembered his therapist's "precise, amused voice," his air of "almost funereal gravity," and his "flair for the last word."

Raised Eyebrows at Yale

To pursue academic medicine, Detre came to the United States in May 1953 and began his Yale career in 1955. In 1956 he married Dr. Katherine Maria Drechsler, like himself a refugee from Hungary. Katherine Detre, MD, DrPH (1926–2006), would build a career as one of the nation's foremost epidemiologists, known internationally for leading large-scale studies investigating the appropriate treatment for cardiovascular disease. Both Detres insisted on the need for evidence-based medical research to evaluate treatments and advance patient care.

At Yale Thomas Detre immediately clashed with the psychoanalysts who dominated the Department of Psychiatry. Yale was not unique: By 1962, analysts would head fifty-nine of the country's eighty-two academic psychiatric departments. "Tom was one of the first to make the leap from psychiatry as an art to psychiatry as medical science," notes Loren Roth, MD, MPH, who trained at Yale under Detre.

Detre envisioned a future in which psychiatrists would go beyond the bounds of their discipline to collaborate with biologists, neurologists, epidemiologists, geneticists, and more, to help people with such biologically and genetically based disorders as depression and schizophrenia.

In 2000 Katherine Detre, MD, DrPh (above), received one of the largest National Institutes of Health grants in University of Pittsburgh history, $52.2 million to fund a nationwide study of how best to treat coronary disease in patients with type 2 diabetes.

At right, Katherine Drechsler married Thomas Detre in 1956. Her husband would later describe the internationally known epidemiologist as his "first recruit" to the University of Pittsburgh and its Graduate School of Public Health.

In 1960 Thomas Detre, MD (seated, right), became director of Psychiatric Inpatient Services at Yale-New Haven Hospital, where he emphasized a multidisciplinary medical approach to psychiatric care and teaching. Seated at left is his Yale colleague Theodore Lidz, MD. Representatives of the company that produced the model of the brain stand behind the two psychiatrists.

THOMAS DETRE: *I think that I was the only person ever promoted to tenure at Yale who was not analyzed. I refused. I told them I was so goddamned healthy, I don't need it!*

Luckily, Yale's chairman of psychiatry was Frederick C. Redlich, MD, a pioneer in social psychiatry who was pushing the department toward a multidisciplinary approach and curriculum. Detre describes Dr. Redlich as "a shining light of American psychiatry. He thought that I was absolutely right, that psychopharmacology was coming."

The first antipsychotic drugs came into use in the early 1950s, offering patients with schizophrenia and psychosis the first chance to lead more normal and fulfilling lives. Many psychiatrists dismissed these drugs as a way of dealing only with symptoms. But Detre predicted they would both improve lives and transform lengthy hospitalization of the mentally ill.

"Tom Detre was one of the first to make the leap from psychiatry as an art to psychiatry as medical science."

— Loren Roth, MD, MPH

Soon he raised eyebrows at Yale not only by treating patients pharmacologically but also by creating Tompkins 1, a boldly experimental psychiatric unit at Yale-New Haven Hospital. Opening in 1960, Tompkins 1 shattered historic assumptions about inpatient psychiatric care. It was the first in the country to apply a therapeutic "patient community" approach to the short-term treatment of acutely ill psychotic patients. On Tompkins 1, hospitalizations that might at one time have lasted several years were reduced to several weeks.

Dr. Detre was in fact one of the first to anticipate the deinstitutionalization of mental patients in the 1960s. "The hospital is not the place for dealing, at a fantastic cost, with the patient's long-term problems," he argued prophetically. "The only purpose of hospitalization, as I see it, is to end hospitalization ... so that the patient [can] manage outside the hospital."

David J. Kupfer, MD, in the early 1970s

"What did Thomas Detre pioneer?" asks Daniel X. Freedman, MD, in *Reflections on Modern Psychiatry*. "At Yale, within a year or two of his arrival in the mid-1950s, Thomas Detre ... turned his pioneering general hospital unit into a lively daily encounter with research as well as treatment." By 1969 Detre's ideas had given rise to fifty-nine published research studies, including one on sleep disturbances by "a gutsy kid from New York," David J. Kupfer, MD.

Detre finished his own controversial, 733-page *Modern Psychiatric Treatment* in 1971. In writing this book, says Dr. Loren Roth, "Tom was 're-medicalizing' American psychiatry, putting it in the mainstream of American medicine. His approach could therefore be appreciated by a medical school, so when a medical school picked a new chairman of psychiatry, they were going to pick somebody who was going to reunite medicine with psychiatry."

Thomas Detre, MD (left), and Henry G. Jarecki, MD (center), present their book, *Modern Psychiatric Treatment*, to Morton F. Reiser, MD (right), who chaired the Department of Psychiatry at the Yale University School of Medicine.

phenothiazine-induced jaundice (Popper 1965), but do have a far more difficult course when they develop an allergic jaundice. Although the eventual *outcome* depends on the extent of the damage (and thus on the rapidity with which the hepatic dysfunction is noted and the drug discontinued), the disorder almost invariably has a benign, self-limiting course. The liver function tests return to normal within a month (though the reversal of the skin discoloration may lag behind), and there have been only 14 deaths reported among the millions of people who have been treated with phenothiazines. In rare instances, when xanthomatous biliary cirrhosis supervenes as a complication, the disorder may last for months (Bolton 1967, Nørredam 1963).

Among the *preventive measures* that have been proposed are weekly urinary bilirubin tests with commercially available reagent kits (The Medical Letter 1968). These provide a very rough screening device that can be performed fairly easily in large mental hospital populations, but are more defensible from the standpoint of expediency than accuracy. Weekly SGOT and alkaline phosphatase measurements are far more reliable, as they make it possible to detect hepatic dysfunctioning fairly early, in any case before the skin discoloration develops (Popper 1959). Minor elevations of SGOT or alkaline phosphatase need not cause alarm, for their values will often return to the baseline without any change in dosage (Wroblewski 1962); if these values continue to rise or the patient becomes jaundiced, the phenothiazine being used must be discontinued immediately. Since with the exception of promazine and chlorpromazine there is no cross-sensitivity, however, it is usually sufficient to change to a different phenothiazine.

BLOOD DYSCRASIAS. Phenothiazines are the leading cause of drug-induced blood dyscrasias. Some patients develop transient leukocytosis, leukopenia, or eosinophilia, but these are usually of no clinical significance (Lomas 1955). Leukocytosis may be due to a wide variety of factors and may even be a result of the anxiety, excitement, and dehydration associated with the disease for which the phenothiazine is being given. If, after the patient is first given a particular drug, his WBC decreases somewhat but reverts to the baseline within a few weeks, this innocuous pattern may repeat itself each time the dosage of that drug is increased. Agranulocytosis, thrombocytopenia, and pancytopenia, on the other hand, are serious complications. A few cases have been reported following the use of thioridazine (Mellaril), trifluoperazine (Stelazine) and others of the piperazine group (Ayd 1961, Dally 1967), but, as with jaundice, the

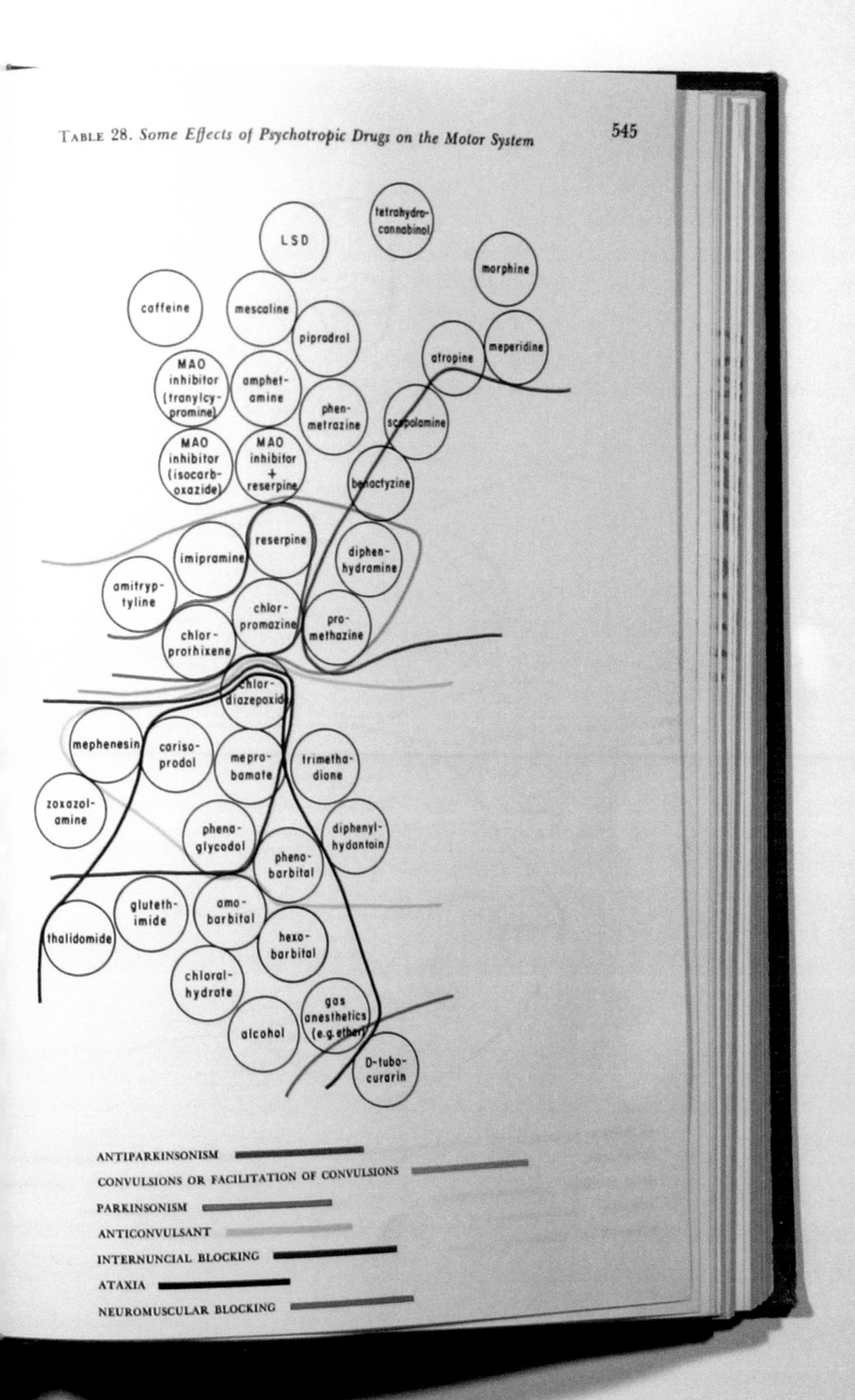

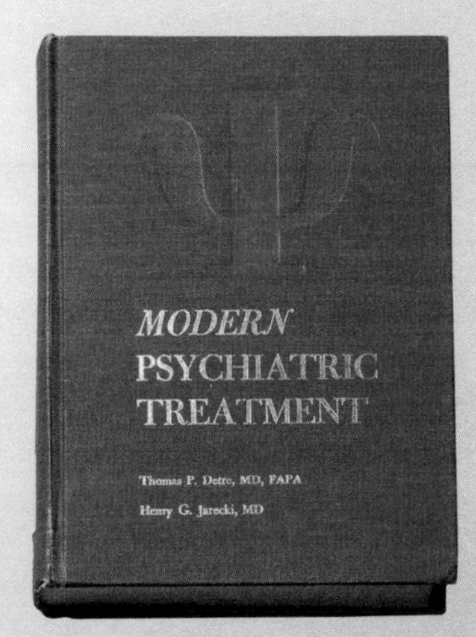

Modern Psychiatric Treatment "re-medicalized" American psychiatry by emphasizing the biological causes of and pharmacological approaches to the treatment of mental illness.

Behind the Times in Pittsburgh

In 1924, the year Thomas Detre was born in Budapest, the Pennsylvania Department of Public Welfare began urging the Commonwealth to build a public psychiatric hospital in Pittsburgh. Only after the University of Pittsburgh, then a private school, donated the land did construction begin in 1938 on Pitt's campus in Oakland, a neighborhood about three miles from downtown Pittsburgh.

The university welcomed the modernistic brick building to its emerging medical center. In the 1920s and 1930s, on a steep rise nicknamed "Cardiac Hill," Pitt was transforming the twelve-acre estate of a locomotive builder into a complex of teaching hospitals – a plan that "insures the perpetual success of ... Pittsburgh as one of the greatest medical centers in the United States," declared an optimistic 1922 fundraising brochure.

Clustered together were Presbyterian, Eye & Ear, Women's, and Children's hospitals. Falk Clinic served as the outpatient facility. Nearby was the Elizabeth Steel Magee Hospital. Also a neighbor, but resisting an affiliation with Pitt, was the Jewish community's Montefiore Hospital, which had opened its own new building in Oakland in 1929. "Such a wealth of material closely assembled does not exist anywhere in the world today," the university maintained.

But architecture is no guarantee of medical excellence. When Western State Psychiatric Hospital opened in 1942, its narrow, localized mission was to train mental health workers for the long-term care of patients in Pennsylvania's state hospitals.

Then came Pittsburgh's nationally known post-World War II renaissance, a sweeping effort to improve the region's economic competitiveness and quality of life. Directing this civic shot in the arm was banker Richard King Mellon, who backed his commitment to Pittsburgh with philanthropic support. When the Richard King Mellon Foundation was created in 1947, one of its first goals was "to establish, maintain, and operate in Pittsburgh a health center of the highest character."

To the Mellons, this meant investing in people. In 1949 the University of Pittsburgh hired psychoanalytic leader Henry W. Brosin, MD, to chair the Department of Psychiatry and direct the psychiatric hospital. In addition, the university took over the management of this hospital, which was renamed Western Psychiatric Institute and Clinic (WPIC). Brosin recruited the nationally known I. Arthur Mirsky, MD, as professor of research psychiatry and director of clinical science, and Benjamin Spock, MD, as professor of child development. "Pittsburgh has taken a long stride toward its goal of becoming one of the world's leading medical centers," boasted the *Pittsburgh Post-Gazette.*

The local soil, however, seemed to lack the nutrients to support such exotic transplants. "Pitt was essentially a backwater in medical education and medical research," recalls Julius S. Youngner, ScD. A pioneer in the science of virology, he arrived from the National Cancer Institute in 1949 as senior scientist in the laboratory of Jonas Salk, MD, where the creation of the live polio vaccine changed history.

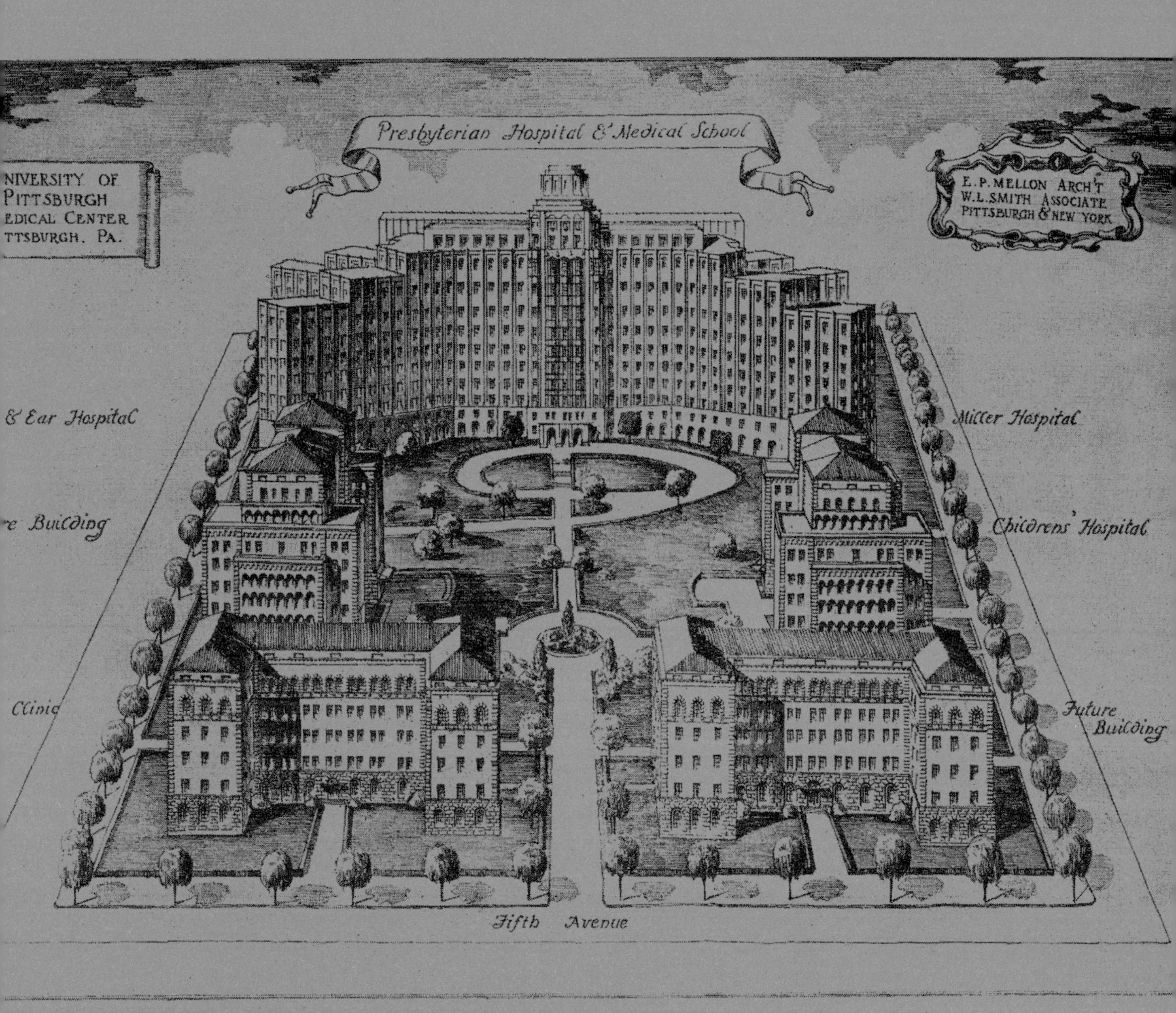

The University of Pittsburgh's "dream of a great medical center" in 1922

JULIUS YOUNGNER: *Don't forget, this was the era before the big entry into the research field by the National Institutes of Health. Most of the medical school faculty – especially clinical faculty – were private physicians who had appointments at the medical school. There were only a limited number of basic scientists who were full time. Departments were very small, very small. There was essentially very little research going on.*

But the Manhattan Project [the U.S. effort during World War II to develop and build an atomic bomb; Dr. Youngner was part of this ultrasecret effort] showed that if you invest money and hire people and build facilities, you can solve problems. And pretty soon the success of the polio vaccine program [generated] worldwide publicity ... and Congress became conscious of what can be done.

Julius S. Youngner, ScD (right), was senior scientist in the Virus Research Laboratory of Jonas Salk, MD (left), at the University of Pittsburgh School of Medicine in the 1950s.

In the Department of Psychiatry, Brosin and Mirsky almost immediately battled for leadership. Soon an iron curtain fell between patient care and research. Dr. Mirsky resigned from the department. He had the locks changed on his lab, where, in self-imposed quarantine, he did landmark studies in the physiology of hypertension. Dr. Spock, the author of the mega-best-selling *Baby and Child Care,* left Pittsburgh to become the pied piper of parenting for the postwar generation. Dr. Brosin, meanwhile, concentrated on psychoanalysis and on developing the Pittsburgh Psychoanalytic Institute. By the time he retired in 1969, academic leaders who visited WPIC concluded that it was too narrowly focused and had fallen behind in the field of psychiatry.

The Commonwealth of Pennsylvania, WPIC's crucial funder, judged the hospital "reactionary, arrogant, and wedded to outmoded values that are in conflict with current welfare concerns." To the outrage of WPIC staff, the university considered

Henry W. Brosin, MD

I. Arthur Mirsky, MD

University of Pittsburgh School of Medicine
Dean Donald N. Medearis Jr., MD

transferring WPIC's management to Presbyterian-University Hospital across the street. In 1970 the university's trustees designated a Committee of the Health Professions to govern the hospital.

By this time two new academic leaders, School of Medicine Dean Donald N. Medearis Jr., MD, and F. Sargent "Sarge" Cheever, MD, Harvard-educated vice chancellor of the schools of the health professions, were eager to strengthen biological psychiatry at Pitt and to make WPIC more responsive to the state. They appealed to the Richard K. Mellon Charitable Trusts for $5 million to create an endowment to attract an outstanding chairman for the Department of Psychiatry.

"The Manhattan Project showed that if you invest money and hire people and build facilities, you can solve problems."

— Julius S. Youngner, ScD

Enter Thomas Detre – to chair the department and to join research, medicine, and psychiatry at the University of Pittsburgh.

"I'll never forget being in my office one day and getting a call from someplace like Bali," remembered George H. Taber, former vice president, director, and trustee of the Richard King Mellon Foundation. "It was Sarge Cheever, just to tell me that Tom would be willing to come."

THOMAS DETRE: *I think the Mellon people had an ultimate idea when they gave that money, at least I thought they did, that they wanted to really see some excellence developing on this campus.*

GEORGE TABER: *Absolutely.*

"Today we concentrate on UPMC and all it's become. But back then, the task was to take this little kernel of Western Psych – and make it into something."

— Hon. Robert J. Cindrich

Transforming the University of Pittsburgh Department of Psychiatry and Western Psychiatric Institute and Clinic

1973–1982

1973 Thomas Detre, MD, officially becomes chairman of the University of Pittsburgh Department of Psychiatry and director of Western Psychiatric Institute and Clinic (WPIC).

Detre appoints Jeffrey A. Romoff as director of the newly formed Office of Education and Regional Programming.

1975 Romoff becomes administrator and associate director of WPIC.

Health care costs in the U.S. rise sharply, fueled by inflation, the growth of private insurance as well as Medicare and Medicaid, advances in technology, and increased use of hospitals.

1970s University of Pittsburgh School of Medicine faculty develop clinical practice plans enabling them to bill patients and collect income apart from their university teaching salaries, and to subsidize the various departments of the school.

Thomas E. Starzl, MD, PhD

1980 Health care expenditures in the U.S. are $255 billion.

Nationwide NIH appropriations rise to $3.4 billion.

The University of Pittsburgh is 36th on the list of NIH grant recipients.

1981 Pioneering liver transplant surgeon Thomas E. Starzl, MD, PhD, is recruited to the University of Pittsburgh.

1982 WPIC takes over the management of the Pittsburgh Child Guidance Center.

The Pittsburgh region loses thousands of manufacturing jobs in the early 1980s. A new economy based on finance, medicine, education, and information begins to emerge.

Scaife Hall, home of the University of Pittsburgh School of Medicine

2

The Leaders and Their Laboratory

"We came here, looked around, and said, incredible! They're living on top of a coal mine, and instead of taking advantage of that great resource they're just growing lettuce! Isn't that ridiculous! I mean, lettuce is nice to eat, but the really valuable and important thing was coal. For us, the only important thing was academic excellence." — Jeffrey A. Romoff

The Vietnam War dragged on during the fall of 1972, George McGovern tried to wrest the presidency from Richard Nixon, and Thomas Detre commuted weekly from New Haven to Pittsburgh, chain-smoking Marlboros through an ebony holder, pacing back and forth in an improvised office, and working to raise the Department of Psychiatry and WPIC "from the ashes."

He had his work cut out for him. "There were no outstanding investigators, no outstanding teaching, no innovation in care," according to Dean Donald Medearis. "There was no modern psychotherapy. There was no basic neurological research." Dr. Gerhard Werner, who chaired the Department of Pharmacology and who would serve as dean of the medical school in the 1970s, said that someone could have been at Pitt "for years without ever knowing there was a Department of Psychiatry."

Somehow, in this unpromising petri dish, Detre believed he could culture one of the first academic departments in the country to focus on biological psychiatry. He envisioned a matrix where emerging knowledge from neuroscience, psychopharmacology, epidemiology, and genetics would fuse with psychiatry in a truly interdisciplinary approach. He wanted to build a department around rigorous clinical research and what would come to be called evidence-based practice – a department that would evaluate psychiatric treatments, improve diagnosis, broaden the understanding of mental illness and other diseases, advance medical education, and give every patient hope.

Even before he officially became chair of Psychiatry on March 1, 1973, Detre began reorganizing WPIC, recruiting researchers and equipping new clinical laboratories. He announced plans to establish specialty clinics. Each would not only improve the quality of and access to patient care, he felt, but also open the doors to more patients – and opportunities for more research.

Accompanying the chairman-elect on his whirlwind visits was one of his former students, David J. Kupfer. After two years on a career-development grant at the National Institute of Mental Health, Kupfer had returned to Yale to pursue research in sleep disorders. In one of the first displays of Detre's legendary talent-scouting, the chairman went out on a limb by inviting the young, relatively inexperienced psychiatrist to direct the new Office of Research at WPIC.

DAVID KUPFER: *Tom had been told correctly by everybody that one of the first things he needed to do was to find a relatively senior director of research, somebody who had already acquired federal grants. So he goes and recruits someone who is thirty-one years old and who has had only a career-development grant! But I didn't feel inferior because there was no research really going on at WPIC, so how could I do badly? I could only go in one direction.*

THOMAS DETRE: *WPIC was an eighteen-story building, three-quarters of which was empty. You know that rule called the baseline of initial values? If something is terribly bad, any improvement is seen as a miracle.*

Dr. Kupfer would go on to succeed Dr. Detre as chairman of Psychiatry in 1983 and to build the department into the nation's number-one recipient of NIH funding for psychiatric research.

Always proud of his "talent-scouting" ability, Thomas Detre, MD (right), recruited a former student, David J. Kupfer, MD (left), to direct WPIC's new Office of Research.

Crisis One: Money

Suddenly, the Pennsylvania Legislature announced that the $2.5 million state appropriation, a critical source of WPIC's annual budget, would be cut in half. Lawmakers argued that WPIC had become an ivory tower, unresponsive to the state's needs. They wanted the hospital to train more psychiatrists in community mental health and better serve less-privileged patients.

THOMAS DETRE: *There was total alienation between the Commonwealth of Pennsylvania and WPIC. But the university at the time had a good lobbyist. He came to see me and said, "I'm here to tell you how this works, but, of course, you will never listen to me." I said, "Not only will I listen to you; I'll go with you to Harrisburg."*

So I went to Harrisburg and talked to people without asking for anything. I offered to help in the way I can help, which is as a medical advisor. "If you get sick, come to us. Here's my telephone number. If you forget it, I'm in the phone book."

Detre convinced the legislators that if they gave him a chance, WPIC would mobilize its resources to serve the people of Pennsylvania. "By the time he got through," Kupfer marvels, "instead of slashing our appropriation, the state had increased it to $3 million."

"Dr. Detre really redefined the relationship between WPIC and the Commonwealth," says George Board, DrPH, a soft-spoken Southerner who worked in government relations for both the psychiatric hospital and later UPMC.

GEORGE BOARD: *Dr. Detre recognized how critical government is to the practice of medicine. So it was really those early days at WPIC that set the foundation for what turned out to be a fairly strong government focus that emerged later within UPMC. They loved him in Harrisburg.*

At the same time, in another shrewd and farsighted move, Detre also pressed for an unusual financial pact allowing the Department of Psychiatry, rather than the School of Medicine, to keep the clinical income generated in WPIC. The chairman would then be free to transfuse the money into the academic mission of research, teaching, and patient care. It was a turning point in the history of the university and for its eventual offspring, UPMC.

George Board, DrPH, helped develop relationships beyond WPIC and psychiatry.

LOREN ROTH: *The most significant thing of all – I mean if it had never occurred, you would have had no UPMC – was that when Tom was recruited here, he became not only the department chairman, he became the director of WPIC. In other words, he became the "owner" of a potentially moneymaking facility.*

JEFFREY A. ROMOFF: *Our ability to keep that clinical money and then reinvest it in the Department of Psychiatry was a defining opportunity for us. It severed us from the bureaucracy of the university and incentivized us to see more patients. It became one of the key economic incentives for excellence.*

Detre also insisted that the Department of Psychiatry be allowed to retain an amount equal to the indirect costs of its researchers' federal research grants from the NIH. He understood that to attract an outstanding research faculty, he needed inducements. "Tom recognized that if you were going to build a research program, you have to return the indirects as a bonus to the worker," observes Richard L. Simmons, MD, Distinguished Service Professor of Surgery and chair emeritus, Department of Surgery at the University of Pittsburgh School of Medicine.

George A. Huber was one of the "fertile minds" on Dr. Detre's young administrative team.

Detre's strategy was entrepreneurial and unexpected. "Customarily, universities control the indirect administrative and capital costs of each grant," explains George A. Huber, a lawyer who joined WPIC in 1975 and later served as UPMC's corporate counsel.

GEORGE HUBER: *The University of Pittsburgh, like most universities, would distribute that overhead how the chancellor's office and the administrators of the university felt it should be best distributed. So you would have to beg to get that indirect dollar back to build new buildings or buy new equipment. Dr. Detre said, "I don't want the university to control that money. We at Western Psych got that money. We should put it into new programs to support our great researchers." The university said, "OK."*

LOREN ROTH: *I rather believe that the first thing Tom negotiated was freedom, freedom to grow WPIC. This is really the origin of UPMC, because this model permitted Tom to recruit researchers, to provide laboratory space and salaries. So Tom applied that principle, that if a researcher can make money, or save money, or be efficient, then the researcher can use those dollars and apply them to the academic mission.*

The bottom line is there were dollars left over from the clinical care enterprise. As long as you have the freedom and autonomy to spend the dollars the way you wanted, you had your own ability to grow academic medicine.

Thomas Detre's first goal – and now UPMC's – was to feed the synergy of research, teaching, and patient care. "Good medicine must be based on good science," he would say in 1987, "and good science, as has been repeatedly proven, is good business." But as George Huber notes, Detre took a big risk by essentially promising the university that his department and WPIC would "stand on our own bottom line."

A Chat That Changed Pittsburgh

Detre knew that to achieve these goals, there would have to be businesslike financial management of the department and especially the hospital. He was one of the first in academic medicine to act on the fact that health care was turning into an industry.

He began recruiting talented managers to staff WPIC. One of his first picks was Vivian Goodman Romoff, RN, MSN, his chief psychiatric nurse at Yale-New Haven. Both he and she had an advanced approach to nursing at that time: they believed that outstanding patient care demanded a strong, collaborative partnership between nurses and physicians. "She was a strong proponent of this approach and had the personality to do it," Detre remembers. "She was a strong role model for nurses. It's one thing to preach it and another to do it."

Vivian Goodman Romoff, RN, MSN. "Her influence here was enormous," says Dr. Detre.

Vivian Romoff would build and lead one of the largest psychiatric nursing services in the country. "Her influence here was enormous," Detre says.

GEORGE HUBER: *Vivian thought outside the box. She was always looking for the perfect nursing model for the treatment of psychiatric patients. She was a tremendous advocate for giving nurses greater responsibility for patient care management. She gave nursing in psychiatry a tremendous kick-start toward modernization. And she could be tough, and demanding; she could be aggressive, she could be political – and she was also a sincerely warm person. Vivian had it all.*

Detre remembers her as "an all-around very attractive person with a great deal of charm. She never used that for anything but to promote patient care. I wanted her to come to Pittsburgh. She said she had a husband, and I thought that was unfortunate," he deadpans. "But I wanted to chat with him."

This "chat" would change Pittsburgh. The twenty-seven-year-old who appeared for an interview in Dr. Detre's New Haven office was Jeffrey A. Romoff – brilliant, brash, hard-driving, idealistic, passionate, witty, iconoclastic, knowledge-hungry, and tempestuous. A self-described "classic trailing spouse," he was a graduate of the historic City College of New York and had recently earned a master's at Yale with a specialty in political science. Now, in 1972, he worked in "a very small mental health counseling planning group in Waterbury, Connecticut."

Under Jeffrey A. Romoff's leadership, UPMC would become the largest fully integrated health enterprise in Pennsylvania and one of the largest nonprofit systems in the nation. He would be cast, like a figure of myth, as both villain and hero, pictured as both the worst thing that ever happened to western Pennsylvania as well

Jeffrey A. Romoff and Vivian Goodman Romoff, RN, MSN. Not yet thirty years old, he followed her to Pittsburgh as a "trailing spouse."

At right, raised in New York amid a family of musicians, Jeffrey A. Romoff (center) has compared organizational leadership to conducting an orchestra.

as its future and savior. And because Romoff rather relishes his image as an outsider, he adds that "either the hostility or the reverence is interesting, but certainly not important."

THOMAS DETRE: *Before I met with him, Jeff sent me a plan he had written for a community mental health center, an application for federal funding. I reviewed that and found it very well put together, so I chatted with him, and I invited him to come to Pittsburgh.*

JEFFREY A. ROMOFF: *Today, Tom politely imagines that he wanted me in my own right. But he can't fool me. It was my wife, Vivian, who he wanted very much to come to Pittsburgh, and he had to take me along with her.*

THOMAS DETRE: *Either you have a good nose for who is going to be superb, or you don't. If you don't, forget about it.*

Trailing Spouse, Synoptic Thinker

Born and raised in the Bronx, Romoff grew up amid a family of musicians and performers and the energy of New York's streets. At the urging of his mother, Evelyn Alter Romoff, he studied for and passed the entrance exam for New York's prestigious Bronx High School of Science. He graduated three hundredth in a class of six hundred. "The personification of mediocrity!" he remembers with disgust.

Again with his mother's support, Jeffrey got a scholarship to City College, alma mater to more Nobel Prize winners than any other public college in the world. There he experienced "a metamorphosis."

JEFFREY A. ROMOFF: *I decided that now that I was going to college, I was going to do it well. And from then on I was a straight-A student. I mean, in everything other than gym.*

But at City College something very important happened, I learned how to read and see the implicit story *in a vast store of information. This actually is the skill I use more than anything now. I am a voracious integrator.*

Why is the story so important? Because it keeps you focused. It identifies the good guys, the bad guys, the places to go; it looks at the mountains; it understands where the potholes are going to be … it lays it all out.

Now, this is not a contrivance. It gives meaning to everything. It gives people place marks for where they are and where they're going. And it gives some actual significance to where they have been.

What I am is basically a synoptic thinker. That's a more elegant way of saying a storyteller.

ROMOFF

Romoff may still have been rough around the edges in 1972, but Detre saw in him the right person to run a keystone program he planned for WPIC. He wanted the hospital to be a "good neighbor." This meant sharing academic resources – knowledge about the latest treatments and approaches to patient care – with health professionals and agencies beyond the bounds of the university.

Together, Detre and his young protégé began inventing an Office of Education and Regional Programming (OERP). To this task, Romoff brought an ability to absorb and distill "a large, large, large amount of information" and to goad people into action. He brought a probing intellect, an unconcealed contempt for mediocrity, and a zeal to fix the world. "I view myself as coming up against whatever is not working right, or is bad," he would say more than thirty years later. "I see myself on a bit of a crusade."

Thomas Detre downplays his achievements, claiming that his strength lies in his "talent-scouting" ability. "Either you have a good nose for who is going to be superb, or you don't," he says. "If you don't, forget about it."

Thomas Detre was no micromanager. When he assigned a job to someone, he expected the individual to go away, do the work fast and exceptionally well, and then get on to the next task. He had confidence that his handpicked lieutenants would succeed. This style suited Romoff's searching spirit perfectly.

GEORGE BOARD: *Our job at OERP was to define a role for WPIC vis-à-vis the publicly funded psychiatric institutions and agencies. And we were to do it at no cost to those public facilities in recognition of the state dollars that WPIC received. This is where Tom's genius really shone, as did Jeff's ability to implement.*

JEFFREY A. ROMOFF: *OERP actually revived and sustained and found a reason for existence for WPIC. It was geared to providing a service to the state, to working with the state hospitals, to working with mental health centers, [and] in doing so successfully, we preserved the state appropriation.*

But when I started, I had never been to a state hospital! I had never worked with state government; I had never lobbied. This is when I really developed the notion that if we could understand something and imagine what it could become, we could make it happen.

Before long OERP had improved the care of psychiatric patients by developing training and consultative programs for mental health providers in twenty-three counties. Romoff and his staff established relationships between state hospitals and community mental health centers. They networked with legislators and community leaders and consulted on drafting state mental health laws. They regularly sent experts to state-run institutions. Vivian Romoff helped develop new nursing programs at state hospitals.

"We got to the point where the Commonwealth would call us in to help quell what were often politically sensitive issues," George Board recalls.

"If Farview State Hospital had a problem, we'd go to Farview," remembers George Huber. "If one of the counties had a problem in mental health, we'd go there and help them out. So Dr. Detre was loved and respected for that reason."

OERP also developed relationships with university departments beyond psychiatry – and with foundations and pharmaceutical companies that could fund academic research. And Romoff, with his wife as assistant director and director of nursing at WPIC, also started to take a broader interest in how the hospital was managed.

JEFFREY A. ROMOFF: *I noticed a whole bunch of things that didn't work. And Vivian would come home every night and say, "Oh my goodness, this is just terrible." So I began the process of getting involved, of saying to Tom that this was a serious problem. Little by little I acquired more responsibility to fix things.*

Romoff became WPIC's administrator and associate director in 1975. He and Detre grew closer. They strategized frequently, often by phone, late into the night.

Analysts Resist

Thomas Detre's cyclonic arrival left many in WPIC reeling. "We at Pitt had never seen anything like the Detre style," admitted the hospital's longtime executive director, Harry N. Dorsey. Detre, too, said he was shocked – at the work ethic of the part-time teaching faculty.

THOMAS DETRE: *There were strange habits here. They came in around 9:15 and then they had their coffee break at 10 or 10:30, then they went to lunch, and by early in the afternoon, you couldn't even find a rummy partner, never mind four for a bridge game! But remember, these habits were not unique to academic departments. This was the general climate.*

Studies in sleep disorders were among the research programs started at WPIC.

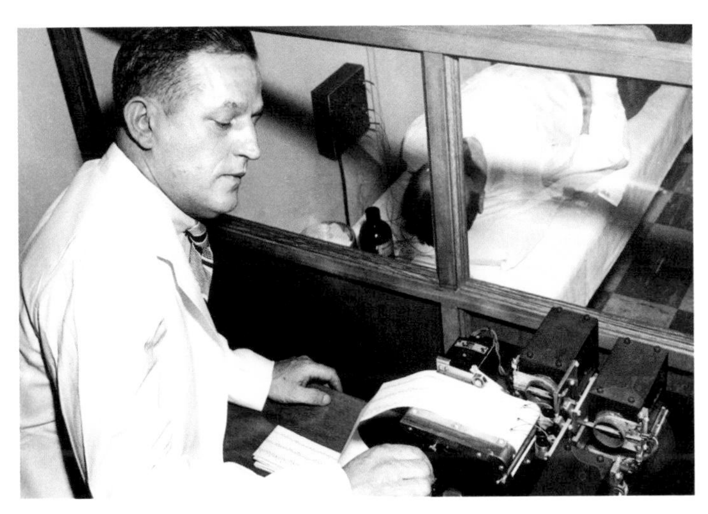

Pushing the faculty to become more productive, Detre insisted that they devote a minimum of twenty-five hours a week to the department. Several members resigned in protest.

Next, members of the Pittsburgh Psychoanalytic Institute, which had thrived in the former regime, resisted his demands for psychiatrists to do clinical research into the lasting value of psychotherapy.

THOMAS DETRE: *There was preliminary evidence that shorter and far less expensive endeavors had produced satisfactory results, [but] you couldn't compare them with long-term psychoanalytic psychotherapy because [the analysts] refused to do anything called clinical trials. They thought that was grossly interfering with the wonderful relationship that patients had with their analysts.*

F. Sargent Cheever, MD, was vice chancellor of the University of Pittsburgh schools of the health professions and an ally of Dr. Detre.

The Psychoanalytic Institute then insisted on appointing its own director, regardless of the chairman's approval. Courteously but firmly, he refused. "The method for selecting a program director … must conform to guidelines established for all University departments," Detre stated in a letter to a university administrator. If the Psychoanalytic Institute wished to remain as an academic program within his Department of Psychiatry, the director would need to have a strong academic research background and a commitment to evaluating the outcomes of psychoanalytic treatment.

"To put it politely, they thought that that was completely outside the pale," Detre remembers. "And I said, well, in that case, ladies and gentlemen, goodbye. I could not negotiate something that was intellectually unacceptable."

Members of the Psychoanalytic Institute took the dispute public, hoping to discredit the new chairman. In what Detre described as a "continued and vigorous communitywide campaign against us," they complained to newspapers, to Dean Medearis, to Vice Chancellor Cheever, and even to Chancellor Wesley W. Posvar that their academic freedom was under threat. Detre, backed by Cheever, retained the university's support. "Sarge Cheever was a charming man," Detre recalls. "And I was very much at home with him because he was exactly like all the people I knew in New Haven."

When the Pittsburgh Psychoanalytic Institute withdrew from the Department of Psychiatry and the university in 1974, Dr. Detre's reputation as an authoritarian was cemented. Acting on his beliefs despite resistance, though, was the only way he had ever known how to be. And although he "won" his first public power struggle in Pittsburgh, the incident marked him among some university administrators, especially in the chancellor's office, as a potentially disruptive character.

THOMAS DETRE: *If you want to make an omelet, you have to break eggs, as they say. And so they were absolutely right that in the first five years I was exceptionally directive and top-down. But my inner ticker told me, rightly or wrongly, that what I and my colleagues tried to do was the right thing to do for this institution; and when you work for an institution, you really have to do your best – because if you don't, everybody loses.*

The Lone Ranger Is Dead

"When my life started at WPIC," Detre remembers, "what I tried to do was to recruit people from various specialties, even other departments, so we could create a robust clinical and research program." Although in the early 1970s he had only a fraction of the budgets of major psychiatric departments like Yale's or Stanford's, the $5 million endowment from the Mellon Charitable Trusts, the increase in the state appropriation, and the promise of new revenue from patient care and research gave him a toehold for the recruiting and collaborations that became his hallmarks. He sought out "academicians who, in addition to being exceptionally competent, have the temperamental characteristics to operate with ease in a multidisciplinary setting without worrying too much about boundaries."

"Dr. Detre knew how to do things on an interdisciplinary basis when nobody was even talking about interdisciplinary," says Gerald S. Levey, MD, executive vice chancellor and provost of Medical Sciences and dean of the David Geffen School of Medicine at UCLA and the former chair of Pitt's Department of Medicine.

THOMAS DETRE: *It was crystal clear to me that you cannot provide decent patient care without basic multidisciplinary research. The time for lone rangers was over. Science was galloping so fast that no single person could grasp it all, alone. So I felt that what made sense was to develop collaborative programs. You collect expertise from everywhere.*

This is the open-door policy that eventually would shape the University of Pittsburgh Cancer Institute, collaborations with Carnegie Mellon University, department mergers, the integration of separate hospitals into a medical center, and the creation of nearly seventy-five interdisciplinary centers of excellence developed during Detre's years at the university. "Inter- and multi-disciplinarity, of course, characterize contemporary biomedical and behavioral research," Senior Vice Chancellor Arthur S. Levine, MD, would say in 2007. But in 1973, such collaboration was far from routine.

Detre pushed psychiatric research into emerging disciplines – biomedicine, neurobiology, social and behavior science, and genetics. His Department of Psychiatry was an early adapter of information technology. He hired electrical engineers and partnered with the Department of Neurology to establish an electroencephalographic unit to provide evidence of how the brain functions. He persisted in breaking through the boundaries between Psychiatry and the rest of the university, despite resistance from the departments of Medicine and Surgery and from the basic sciences, where Psychiatry and WPIC were regarded as second-class citizens. He established collaborations with the departments of Sociology, Psychology, Clinical Psychology, Neurosurgery, Pharmacology, Biochemistry, and Life Sciences, as well as the School of Law.

THOMAS DETRE: *Before long the Department of Psychiatry was referred to as "the other medical school across the street," because whatever was missing in the medical school, we tried to compensate for the deficit.*

In exercising his talent-scouting abilities, "He had an uncanny instinct for spotting 'stars' and potential stars," writes Meyer Sonis, MD, who was a child psychiatrist at WPIC when Detre arrived.

Why did people follow him?

LOREN ROTH: *Tom first of all was a very seductive man who has a great deal of personal charm and was able to communicate very quickly to people that he really wanted to change things. I mean, this was the early 1970s – everybody wanted to change things! I did.*

"I came here with some trepidation," says Lila Decker, RN, who served as Detre's original "point lady, troubleshooter, confidante, and manager."

"Everyone at Yale told me I was a fool to go away with Dr. Detre. 'You know, he's a ruthless Hungarian,' and those were the words that they used. And I said I'm willing to gamble. We came, we saw, he conquered," she quips.

One of Detre's "seven commandments for recruitment" was to "avoid candidates who need more than six hours of sleep a night." He worked about sixteen hours a day and he expected his associates to do the same. He adroitly picked vibrant, energetic people with the intellectual flexibility to move into new positions and take on new responsibilities.

Lila Decker, RN, came from Yale in 1973 to act as Dr. Detre's "point lady," and she stayed with WPIC and UPMC throughout her career.

Diane P. Holder, who would become president of WPIC and later executive vice president, UPMC; president, Insurance Services Division; and president and CEO, UPMC Health Plan, was a psychiatric social worker when she interviewed for a job at WPIC in 1980.

DIANE HOLDER: *Dr. Detre interviewed me because Dr. Detre interviewed every single person who was going to touch a patient. He interviewed you for your character and your spirit and your gut. Were you the kind of person who had whatever it was he thought you needed to have?*

Claudia Roth, PhD, was a young, ambitious undergraduate psychology student when she interned at WPIC in the 1980s. The day after she graduated she was offered a job there, and she went on to complete two master's degrees and a PhD while working full time. When Detre interviewed her in 1989 to be project coordinator on a major,

$5 million grant, "He asked me if I required much sleep," she reminisces. "He also asked me where I saw myself in five years or ten years." Dr. Roth would go on to become president of WPIC and vice president, Behavioral Health Services, UPMC.

Dr. Detre recruited science writer Margaret C. McDonald, PhD, in 1983.

Margaret C. McDonald, PhD, who would become an associate vice chancellor for Academic Affairs, was a writer for the American Psychiatric Association when Detre invited her to work with him at WPIC.

MARGARET MCDONALD: *Tom had a famous line when he was trying to recruit people to Pittsburgh, and that was, "Vell, just come look." And, of course, they'd get you here in the dead of night; you drive through the Fort Pitt Tunnel and see the miraculous view. You go to a nice restaurant, then have a marathon day of interviews, and then off to the plane again. You go home and say, "You know what? Pittsburgh was pretty nice."*

George Board was completing his Air Force Medical Service Corps commitment in San Antonio, Texas, when Detre urged him to join OERP in 1976. "I actually laughed at him," remembers Board, who had intended to return to the University of North Carolina. "But he said, 'Look. Just come up with your wife and enjoy our hospitality for two or three days.' When I emerged from that tunnel in the late afternoon, it was as if Dr. Detre had orchestrated the whole thing. The sun was shining, and the buildings were lit up. It was just gorgeous. And when we got to Oakland, everything was arranged, including interviews for my wife at the Graduate School of Public Health and for me as well to complete my studies there."

And sometimes getting people to WPIC took a miracle. Pittsburgh's potential intrigued Dr. David Kupfer, who found the city in 1972 "a place where young people could move rather quickly." Nevertheless, he feared that leaving the prestige of Yale could wreck his career.

DAVID KUPFER: *I was in New Haven debating about whether to come here or not, and I'm watching a Steelers game on television. That's the game where the pass is thrown to Franco Harris – the "Immaculate Reception." And I turned to my family and said, "You know something? We're going to Pittsburgh." I'm big on signs. I knew one when I saw it.*

"I learned a lot from Tom Detre," remarks Clifford E. Brubaker, PhD, dean of the School of Health and Rehabilitation Sciences. "Tom said, 'I try to find someone intelligent and put them in position, and I watch them. If they do a good job, I encourage them more. If they don't, I wave goodbye.' All his judgments, and I think you can say this about Jeff too, are based on, 'This is what we have to do to make this machine work.'"

Driving the Clinical Machine

Conceivably, Thomas Detre and Jeffrey A. Romoff could distill their careers into eleven words: *Utilize your current resources to create something that's better and bigger.* In the 1970s they recognized that demands by government and business to control health care spending would force a major paradigm shift. They predicted that health care would be just as subject to the marketplace as any other business or industry. To make WPIC more efficient and to increase its patient base, they recruited astute managers to run the hospital.

DAVID KUPFER: *The unique ingredient of the experiment here in Pittsburgh is that an equal amount of attention was paid to driving the clinical machine as the academic machine. If you don't have patient populations, you can't really carry out significant clinical research.*

Interestingly, not one of Detre's administrative recruits was trained in hospital administration. He wanted people who could look through new prisms at the challenges of health care management. He and Romoff looked for managers who could cross-fertilize the ideas of physicians, scientists, accountants, lawyers, and other skilled specialists. They sought out colleagues with excellent interpersonal skills and a high tolerance for ambiguity.

"Our colleagues were energized, exciting people," attorney George Huber remembers. "I really felt like I was doing something worthwhile. Everybody was – and still is – bright, loyal, working toward a common goal. It was just exciting, not run-of-the-mill."

"At WPIC," says Kupfer, "intelligence – both social intelligence as well as other kinds of intelligence – would be the main criteria."

The energy on WPIC's sixth-floor management offices was contagious.

MARGARET MCDONALD: *Jeffrey and Loren [Roth] would have conversations from one end of the floor to the other, so you couldn't not listen because it was just shouted across the floor.*

GEORGE HUBER: *Jeff would take Tom's and his own ideas and discuss them with all of us, in what was called the management meeting, and we would debate them for hours – what we thought would work or wouldn't work, just think through them. It was fun – arguing with one another, disagreeing, and looking for other ways of doing it. And then he would say, "Let's try it this way."*

DIANE HOLDER: *There was always real vision there in terms of asking, "What is the next generation of medicine? Where should we be going?" And trying to figure out, "OK, now that I know where that road is, where am I going to get the money to make sure that I can make that happen?"*

GEORGE BOARD: *We were constantly, constantly innovating – innovating not just in science but also in administrative practices and in the delivery models.*

"There was always a frontier mentality," says Jane Duffield, hired by Detre as public relations director of WPIC in 1976, "always pushing forward." At WPIC her assignment was to build WPIC's reputation "beyond the Greater Pittsburgh Airport."

GEORGE BOARD: *I always compared Tom Detre and Jeff Romoff in those days to the scientist and the engineer. Dr. Detre was the theoretician. Romoff was the strategist who implemented the vision. Jeff was challenging. You never felt comfortable that you were on top of your game, with either Jeff or Dr. Detre. You'd get an A on the paper, so to speak, and Jeff would ask, "Why isn't it an A+? What are you going to do tomorrow?"*

I would tell folks that we were recruiting, "This is the most exciting yet challenging place you'll ever work. You will develop some neuroses, but you will have fun while you're doing it."

RICHARD SIMMONS: *They created an institution where your talents can be realized, and that is the very best thing that can happen to people.*

GEORGE HUBER: *Everybody was in awe of Dr. Detre. He's extremely articulate and quick on his feet, and he's a psychiatrist. Tom and Jeff were able to read people very quickly, and to know what makes them tick and how to motivate them. They know where you're coming from as soon as you open your mouth. And they were always respectful to other ideas and points of view.*

Both David J. Kupfer, MD (left), and Carol M. Anderson, PhD (right) — author, researcher, teacher, clinician, and mental health administrator — were among the "Yale mafia" who followed Dr. Detre to Pittsburgh.

LILA DECKER: *Tom was probably the most effective boss anybody could ever have. He said, "I have a few demands. I need you to be accountable. I need you to be in my brain. And I need to have you act professionally." And I thought, "How am I ever going to get in his brain?" But he taught me how to do that, which is, if you have a question, if you ever questioned what he's thinking, then you ask him, which is so simple.*

"He just got past all the superficial things," says Carol M. Anderson, PhD, professor of Psychiatry and Social Work at WPIC, who also began working with Detre at Yale. "You always knew exactly where you stood. If you were not in good standing, you either got out, or you changed in some way to be more productive or more creative."

"I can't emphasize enough the excitement of having a meeting with Tom Detre, Jeff Romoff, and George Huber back in those days," remembers Robert J. Cindrich, who would succeed Huber as UPMC's chief legal counsel in 2004. "These guys had fertile minds, and they would always be thinking up things."

"Dr. Detre and Dr. Kupfer would go down to the National Institute of Mental Health, talk, and get involved in various study sections," says Huber. "And it wasn't all 'give me, give me, give me.' It was 'how can we help you?' And so they gained their confidence."

"They kept their eyes open for every nickel of grant money – usually federal, that was available, stuff that no one paid any attention to before," Cindrich remembers. WPIC established an Office of Research Consultation, recruiting bright people who knew how to write grants, and then had those people teach other people how to go after federal monies and get a grant funded. *The Wall Street Journal* would find WPIC's "boot camps on grant writing" still innovative thirty years later.

And Detre continually tested the bounds of his managers' abilities with nonstop talent-scouting. Paying for this brainpower, in large part, was the clinical revenue from WPIC.

GEORGE HUBER: *We used to get so upset with Dr. Detre! He was always out recruiting some faculty person and promising them a dowry that would just drive us nuts. We would be trying to be cost conscious – you know, we're not going to make our budget and he'd come back and say, "I'm hiring Dr. X, and he's at Harvard right now, or she's at Harvard right now, they're coming in, and you better find $X million to fund their war chest."*

> *"From a business point of view, WPIC went from nothing to a very profitable organization that reinvested in itself. Our ability to reinvest that clinical money in the Department of Psychiatry ... became one of the key driving economic incentives for excellence."*
>
> — Jeffrey A. Romoff

"I've always called WPIC the mouse that roared," laughs Cindrich.

From the Top You See Taller Mountains

Against all odds, WPIC grew in national prominence. Within four years of Detre's arrival, the National Institute of Mental Health designated WPIC a Clinical Research Center for Affective Disorders. The hospital established the John Merck Program for multiply disabled children, the only one of its kind in the country. Within ten years the University of Pittsburgh Department of Psychiatry would rank as one of the nation's three top recipients of NIH psychiatric funding. Between 1974 and 1982 the department's full-time faculty increased from thirty-six to close to a hundred and fifty. WPIC's staff grew from three hundred to twelve hundred.

GERALD LEVEY: *Tom built Western Psych into the best psychiatric hospital and department in the United States. There is no question about that; he built a powerhouse.*

Increasingly outstanding people in turn attracted larger and larger amounts of funding for research, a cycle which led to more patients, more students, and more advanced care and teaching. This cycle set the pattern for UPMC.

By 1983 WPIC had become one of the largest university-based, clinical, educational, and research facilities in the United States. In 2000 the building would be dedicated Thomas Detre Hall of the Western Psychiatric Institute and Clinic.

In time WPIC would rank among *U.S. News & World Report*'s "Best of the Best" psychiatric care providers in the United States. WPIC and the Department of Psychiatry, housing six federally funded centers of excellence, would regularly place first nationally in psychiatric research funding from NIH. And a front-page article in *The Wall Street Journal* would discuss the "resentment" that Pitt's success had engendered among its research university competitors – including Yale.

JEFFREY A. ROMOFF: *What we did at WPIC was to take an absolutely irrelevant, dead institution that had never done anything interesting in health care, certainly not in psychiatry, and make it into a gem: a number-one institution academically and a number-one institution in terms of community psychiatry.*

[But] it would be wrong to say that when Tom and I arrived, we imagined anything other than to make a great academic department of psychiatry. That was at the heart of what we wanted to do, and to have an excellent psychiatric hospital.

As the years progressed, our scope and sense of the issues increased. I view it as climbing a mountain. The higher you get, the more you see. By the time you get to the top of the mountain, what you really see – which is always a bit disconcerting – is a whole bunch of taller mountains.

"We intentionally and aggressively intervened to blur traditional boundaries between departments, schools, and hospitals to ensure high-quality patient care and to enhance opportunities for interdisciplinary education, research, and research training."

— Thomas Detre, MD

Steering the University of Pittsburgh toward the synergy of research, teaching, and patient care — to provide "the care of tomorrow before tomorrow dawns"

1982 – 1990

1982 Thomas Detre, MD, becomes associate senior vice chancellor for Health Sciences at the University of Pittsburgh. He and his associates set out to apply the WPIC model to the School of Medicine, and begin to plan interdisciplinary, interinstitutional centers of excellence.

1983 Congressional legislation changes reimbursement from "reasonable cost" to flat-rate prospective payment for Medicare inpatient hospital services, forcing hospitals to operate more efficiently. In a time of economic recession in western Pennsylvania, both demand for hospitalization and the resources available to pay for it are significantly reduced.

1984 University of Pittsburgh Chancellor Wesley W. Posvar appoints Dr. Detre senior vice chancellor for Health Sciences and interim dean of the School of Medicine.

1985 Ronald B. Herberman, MD, is recruited from the National Cancer Institute to direct the University of Pittsburgh Cancer Institute (UPCI).

1990 The National Cancer Institute designates UPCI a comprehensive cancer center. UPCI is the youngest cancer center ever to receive this prestigious designation.

Established in 1985 as the Pittsburgh Transplantation Institute, the Thomas E. Starzl Transplantation Institute was renamed in 1996 in honor of the modern-day father of organ transplantation.

International competition and higher production and labor costs in the early 1980s led to many plant closings in the Pittsburgh region, a devastating loss for the proud Steel City. Dr. Detre believed that health care, education, and research could offer the potential base for a new economy.

3

A New Ecology

"Tom Detre got the jump on everyone. He knew before anyone else that health care progress – and maybe even all scientific progress – was made at the juncture where disciplines cross boundaries." — Loren Roth, MD, MPH

Two roads diverged in 1982 for Dr. Thomas Detre: He could stay in Pittsburgh or return to the prestige of the Ivy League. "I'm not a maintenance man," he says. "Once you accomplish about 80 percent of what you want to accomplish, the time must come to exit." Detre's remarkable success at recruiting researchers and attracting research funding had made him a hot academic property. An offer to chair a major New York university's psychiatry department intrigued him in 1982, particularly because he felt fed up with the obstruction and exasperating scrutiny he and his associates were subjected to by the University of Pittsburgh's administrators.

"Some of Chancellor Posvar's lieutenants tried to stifle us," he maintains. Wesley W. Posvar had graduated first in his class at West Point and was a brigadier general in the U.S. Air Force. His staff had a high regard for military discipline, and they enforced order as they pulled Pitt out of debt between 1967 and the late 1970s.

"Control and hierarchy were the methods of organization that these administrators understood, and that's really what they imposed upon faculty," agrees George Huber, himself a distinguished graduate of the United States Naval Academy. "They did their very best to discredit Dr. Detre and Jeff in the mind of Chancellor Posvar."

Romoff, who liked to cast himself and Detre in the role of the university's "perennial pariahs," contends that these adversaries "were as ineffective in [quashing] us as they were at mining Pitt's resources."

"With the decline of heavy industry in the [Pittsburgh] region, the upgrading of biomedical science and the broadening of clinical excellence are essential for competing [and are] one of the few ways by which we could favorably impact on the economy of this city within a reasonably short period of time."

— Thomas Detre, MD

What Will You Do for an Encore?

Despite his staff's attempts to rein in the "WPIC mafia," Chancellor Posvar saw that Detre and his colleagues had the vision and ability to advance the University of Pittsburgh academically and financially.

THOMAS DETRE: *So Posvar said, if you go to another university, what are you going to do for an encore? You have built an outstanding department of psychiatry here; could doing that again be really that interesting? So why don't you just stay and do something with the medical school and the health sciences and the hospitals? They need help.*

"Part pragmatist, part philosopher," Thomas Detre at fifty-eight was perhaps more able and captivating than ever. With his deep, satiny voice, dark, appraising eyes, and graying hair combed back from a broad forehead; with his courtly manners, Italian suits, and ever-present cigarette holder, he radiated authority. His habit of wearing his topcoat over his shoulders like a cape, combined with his Hungarian accent, inevitably gave rise to muttered jokes about Count Dracula. "I think he used that image, played it to get people to collaborate," laughs Julius Youngner, Distinguished Service Professor Emeritus of Molecular Genetics and Biochemistry. Detre seemed also tireless, and he could be an electrifying speaker. "I was fascinated by how much information he can convey in so few words," remarks Dean Clifford Brubaker.

Wesley W. Posvar, PhD, served as chancellor of the University of Pittsburgh from 1967 to 1991.

Detre was also ambitious to finish what he had started – to continue moving the University of Pittsburgh toward his vision of academic medical excellence: creating synergy between research, teaching, and patient care. The first step toward that synergy was interdisciplinary collaboration; the second was recruiting outstanding people. Detre saw recruiting as venture capital – an investment in Pittsburgh and better medical care.

An annual month in Maine gave Drs. Thomas and Katherine Detre the chance to relax, fish, think, and plan.

Weighing Options

In August 1982, Thomas and Katherine Detre retreated as usual to their summer place in Maine. There he could take his boat out to the middle of the lake and fish. The late George Taber, who would serve as chair of UPMC for eighteen years, once asked his friend what he caught. "I don't catch anything," Detre replied. "It gives me a chance to be alone and think."

That August in Maine he thought about the challenges he would face as a university administrator for the health sciences. The federal government was slashing the budget for Medicare and Medicaid, and funding for medical research was not a priority at that time. Detre knew he would have to continue to battle hostile camps within his own university as well as the "fiefdoms" of each independent teaching hospital. And beyond the university's Oakland campus an emerging competitor was on the rise. Allegheny General Hospital had been able to "mobilize its fiscal resources and political support" to outpace any of the university-related hospitals. Strong community hospitals like Shadyside and West Penn also loomed as rivals just a couple of miles beyond the university's ivory towers.

But Detre and the WPIC managers believed that by raising the academic quality of the University of Pittsburgh, they could also help the Pittsburgh region. A prestigious academic medical center, they predicted, could bring world-class health care to western Pennsylvania; attract researchers, clinicians, and research funding; and spin off new companies in the emerging biotechnology and biomedical fields.

They knew that the Pittsburgh region, stunned in the early 1980s by a hemorrhage of manufacturing jobs, desperately needed an economic transfusion – and it needed hope. Detre knew a lot about loss, and he had a prescription: Move into new territory. Take risks. Cross borders. Dream big and act boldly.

When Detre returned from Maine at the end of August, he had decided to stay – and create a new ecology for Pittsburgh.

Building a House of Few Walls

On October 6, 1982, Chancellor Wesley Posvar announced Detre's appointment as associate senior vice chancellor for the Health Sciences, with "responsibilities" in the schools of Medicine, Dental Medicine, Nursing, Pharmacy, the health-related professions, and the Graduate School of Public Health.

With his keen grasp of politics, Detre began his new job by turning to the network of allies he had cultivated both inside and outside the university. His achievements at WPIC, for instance, had earned the confidence of the trustees of the Richard King Mellon Foundation, the largest of the city's important philanthropies. This foundation had what he described as "the financial and moral power and the leadership" to influence the development of biomedical advances in Pittsburgh.

Along with other civic leaders, banker Richard King Mellon, his family, his foundation, and its trustees had shown a longtime commitment to strengthening and diversifying the economy in western Pennsylvania and improving the quality of health care. By 1982 the Mellons had contributed millions of dollars to the University of Pittsburgh schools of the health sciences. A major gift to the Department of Surgery had supported the recruitment of Henry T. Bahnson, MD, from Johns Hopkins to chair the department in 1963. "Hank" Bahnson, a big, hugely talented surgeon and a risk-taker who had climbed the Matterhorn, performed Pennsylvania's first heart transplant in 1968.

It was Bahnson who invited his old friend Thomas E. Starzl, MD, PhD, to start a liver transplant program at Pitt in 1981, when organ transplantation was still in its infancy. Starzl, whom Dr. Richard Simmons calls "the greatest surgeon of the twentieth century," put together an interdisciplinary team of surgeons, immunologists, pharmacologists, and other biomedical scientists. The University of Pittsburgh Transplantation Institute (renamed the Thomas E. Starzl Transplantation Institute in 1996) would make Pittsburgh the largest organ transplant and research center in the world.

Yet the university had so far failed to fulfill the 1920s vision of a "great academic medical center for Pittsburgh." No one had been able to unite the schools of the health sciences and the Oakland teaching hospitals into a true "community and regional health resource." With their fiercely independent cultures,

Henry T. Bahnson, MD

Two famous surgical pioneers and longtime friends, Henry T. Bahnson, MD (left), and Thomas E. Starzl, MD, PhD (right), during a rare break in the action in the 1980s

powerful trustees, entrenched medical staffs, and turf-protecting administrators, the hospitals would not be corralled.

So Detre and Romoff tried a different play, a sort of end run. If they couldn't knock down the barriers between the hospitals and the university by force, they would create a new entity: interdisciplinary, "inter-university" centers of excellence.

These centers – first of all collaborative – would integrate the best research, clinical care, and teaching from various departments, hospitals, and institutions. The centers would bypass politics and turf defense by joining participants under a matrix management structure not unlike WPIC's, where interdisciplinary groups regularly combined on projects.

Funding for the centers of excellence would be channeled through the University of Pittsburgh, and each center director would report to the university through Detre, who would be on hand to arbitrate any disagreements. "That was a very good idea because nobody would come to me," he remarks dryly. "They always resolved all of their problems." Nobody wanted a "Detre haircut."

The most visible center of excellence would focus on cancer research and treatment, the area Detre believed held the most promise for improving Pittsburgh's quality of life and attracting new funding. He also planned corollary centers for nuclear magnetic resonance imaging and molecular biology and genetics, as well as a new MD/PhD program to be run jointly by the University of Pittsburgh and Carnegie Mellon University (CMU). He predicted that collaboration between MDs and PhDs – between clinical care and laboratory research – would lead to "tangible bench-to-bedside outcomes."

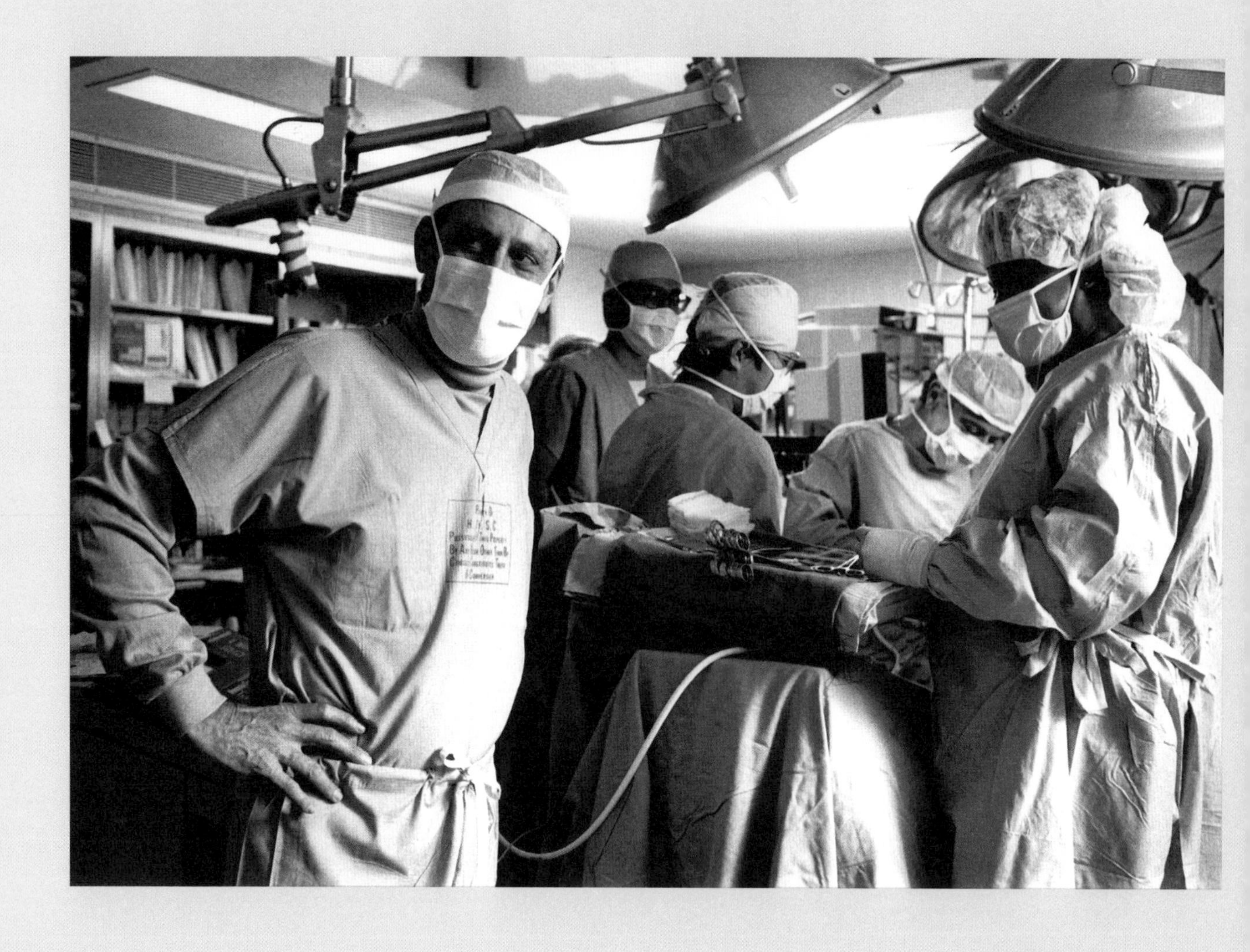

Thomas E. Starzl, MD, PhD

The pioneering liver transplant surgeon came to the University of Pittsburgh in 1981. He and his multidisciplinary team built the world's largest liver transplant program and developed the Pittsburgh Transplantation Institute, renamed the Thomas E. Starzl Transplantation Institute in 1996. "In our university and professional lives, I feel that we are in a crusade, not a business," he wrote in a letter to Henry T. Bahnson, MD, in 1981.

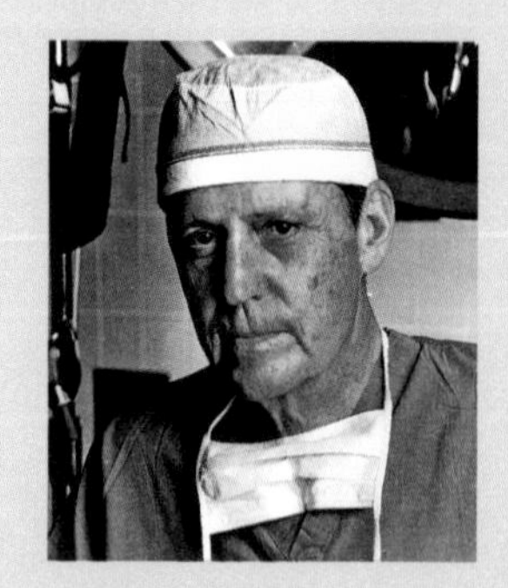

Dr. Detre and Carnegie Mellon University President Richard M. Cyert, PhD (right), broke the boundary between their two campuses to develop important collaborative programs that built Pittsburgh as a research center.

Although CMU sat just across Panther Hollow from Pitt, an invisible fence had seemed to divide the neighboring campuses. But Detre saw CMU as a resource to be tapped. He built on his friendship with President Richard M. Cyert, PhD, who was propelling CMU to national prominence in such groundbreaking fields as robotics and software engineering.

THOMAS DETRE: *Cyert was very knowledgeable, rather quiet, unpretentious, well informed, sharp. He did not waste time or words. And he never spoke of himself. He always spoke about the issue – what needs to be done, why, and how. I went over to see him. We talked for three minutes, and in five minutes I was out of his office; every detail was settled; and we were on the way.*

And so this process [of creating] interdisciplinary centers of excellence started at the University of Pittsburgh and it crossed the university to CMU because Dick Cyert and I were temperamental soul mates. Both he and I had a good idea of what the future would be.

Seeding UPMC

"From my point of view," said George Taber, "the Richard King Mellon Foundation was instrumental in encouraging cooperation through the Pittsburgh Cancer Institute, and the Pittsburgh Cancer Institute is the real beginning of UPMC." George Taber directed the foundation in the 1980s.

Cancer was personal to Thomas Detre and Jeffrey A. Romoff. Detre "thought it was ridiculous" that when a patient or a friend called him for advice about cancer treatment, "I have to send them either to Boston or New York or somewhere else." And now, in 1982, his chief nurse and dear friend, Vivian Romoff, was fighting an aggressive form of breast cancer. She would die in 1983 at the age of thirty-seven ... while her husband worked with passion to plan a cancer center for Pittsburgh.

When Detre became associate senior vice chancellor for the Health Sciences, a committee was already exploring an institute for cancer treatment at Presbyterian-University Hospital. The group submitted a report, but Detre rejected it in disgust. It "totally overlooked the investigational aspects of cancer diagnosis and treatment, a component which is absolutely essential to differentiate a university-based cancer center from patient care services situated in major community hospitals throughout the nation," he wrote to George Taber.

"Tom and I decided, under Tom's direction, that the only place where a cancer center really could be housed was the university, in cooperation with CMU and the various hospitals," Taber would recall.

Detre drafted Gerald Levey and Bernard Fisher, MD, to co-chair a new planning committee. He assigned Romoff to make sure their work pressed ahead.

Fisher, an iconoclastic surgeon and researcher, had performed the first kidney transplants in Pittsburgh, "in the sixties, when the chairman of the Department of Medicine at that time thought that this was an immoral thing," he remembers. As chair of the Pittsburgh-based National Surgical Adjuvant Breast and Bowel Project (NSABP) from 1967 to 1994, Fisher revolutionized breast cancer research and treatment. He suggested, based on NSABP studies, that breast cancer is a systemic disease that metastasizes unpredictably. He proposed that the standard treatment could become lumpectomy plus systemic chemotherapy, not disfiguring mastectomy.

JEFFREY A. ROMOFF: *Bernie Fisher was way ahead of his time. And Bernie by the way was an isolate in modern surgery when he was telling everyone that lopping off breasts really wasn't right. You can imagine the response to that.*

Gerald S. Levey, MD

Bernard Fisher, MD

Bernard Fisher, MD (left), who performed the first kidney transplant in Pittsburgh in 1964, is best known for laboratory investigation that revolutionized the treatment of breast cancer. Timothy R. Billiar, MD, chair of the Department of Surgery, describes Dr. Fisher's advances as "among the most important contributions ever made to women's health."

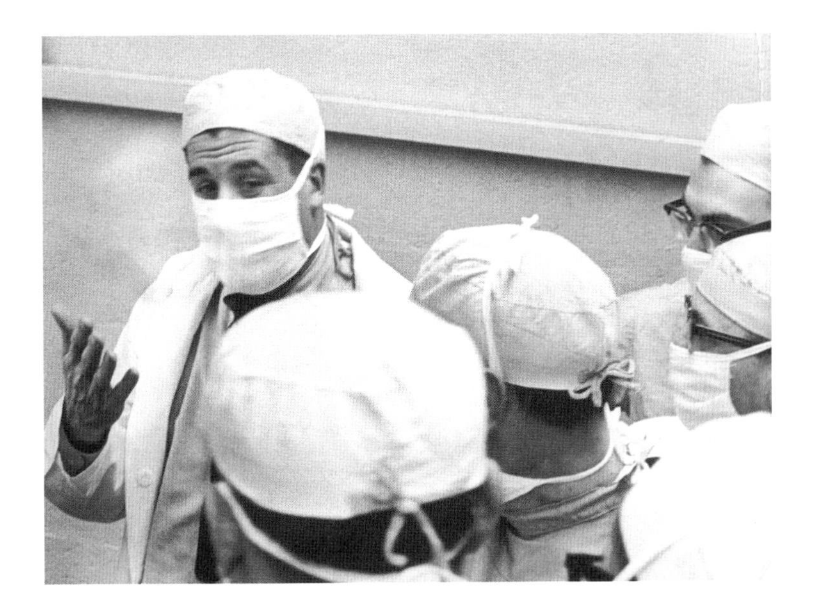

He and Levey were to come up with a report. I said, "Bernie, give me all your files. Give me everything that there is about academic cancer centers." And then I talked to him, I learned from him, I took all the things he wanted to do, and wrote the report.

And when Vivian had breast cancer, I did the same thing with everything that was ever written about breast cancer. Virtually everything. There it was a life and death story, and I lost it. Vivian lost it. But I lost, too.

In 1983 this Detre-Romoff-Fisher-Levey plan recommended that a Pittsburgh cancer center should transcend all barriers, including those between Pitt and CMU. It should have its administrative base in the University of Pittsburgh (Detre and his university-employed WPIC managers), "thus assuring equal status for all participating hospitals, departments, and schools."

Importantly, the new plan also gave Detre the power to "tax" the university-related hospitals that chose "to participate in the creation of a comprehensive cancer center." They would be obliged "to provide funds both for the central core and revolving discretionary funds earmarked for research and development." Detre had helped to create a similar system at Yale, taxing the earned income of clinical departments to get money for research in the basic sciences. Implicitly this strategy pushed the various university and hospital factions and fiefdoms into a cooperative venture, and it guaranteed start-up funds until the center could earn its own income.

The plan predicted that the cancer center would generate research funds, create jobs, train health professionals, act as a catalyst for all hospitals to upgrade services, attract venture capital, and lead to new construction.

Every prediction would come true.

J. WRAY CONNOLLY: *My principal memory [of Dr. Detre], other than the affection that I developed for him over the years, was that when he made up his mind to do something, it would be done. He would meet with people, discuss it. One of the things he talked to me about was his vision for a cancer center. For some reason I thought we were biting off more than we should chew, or could chew at that time. But it didn't matter. He was going to have a cancer center. We do – and it is world-class.*

Beyond start-up funding, Detre in September 1983 asked the Richard King Mellon Foundation to back him personally in his efforts to bring the universities and the Oakland hospitals closer. "I believe that a private conversation between the leadership of the foundation and the two university presidents, encouraging them to pursue joint ventures, would have a most salutary effect on future developments," Detre wrote to Taber.

In December 1983 George Taber informed Chancellor Posvar that the Richard King Mellon Foundation would make an initial grant of $3 million, on condition that CMU, the hospitals, and the foundation would have a distinct role in the direction of policy at the cancer center *and* that Dr. Detre would be responsible for its performance and governance. (The Mellon Foundation would contribute an additional $3 million in 1986 and $8 million in 1989 for the cancer center.)

Buoyed by this support, Detre used $100,000 from his own budget to call together a committee of national specialists to start a search for the right cancer center director.

THOMAS DETRE: *I knew a great deal about mood disorders, but heaven knows I didn't know anything about oncology. But before I recruited, I always went to the library and spent several weeks reading, learning what the field is, who is who, what is what, what is going to happen, what is likely to happen – not today but tomorrow.*

The search committee's first candidate was a cancer specialist who was interested in chemotherapy protocols. After talking to him, I told the committee that that cancer treatment reminds me of Mr. Magoo. Remember Mr. Magoo? The cartoon character. He sits in his office. He's half blind. And he suddenly hears a fly buzzing around. He takes a machine gun and starts shooting at it! This cannot be the future of cancer here, I felt. I told the committee we need to bring in somebody else.

So in came Dr. Ronald Herberman, whom I liked instantly because he had a very good grasp of the modern science, which was not yet ready for human consumption, but it represented the future.

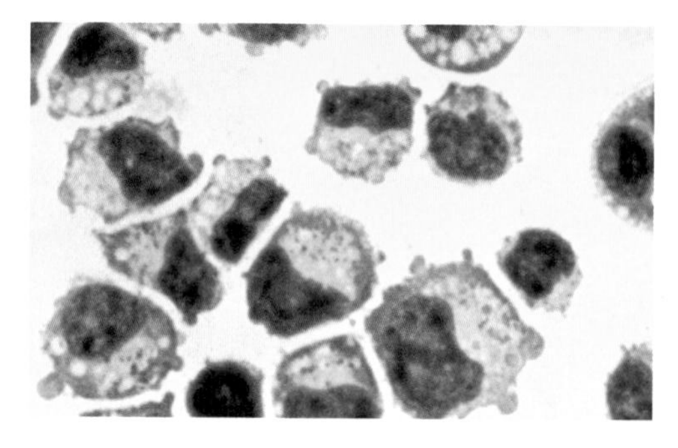

In the laboratory of Ronald B. Herberman, MD, pioneering investigations of natural killer (NK) cells in the 1970s demonstrated that they play an important role in resistance to the metastatic spread of cancer.

Ronald B. Herberman, MD, an internationally recognized tumor immunologist who had made major contributions to research on "natural killer" (NK) cells, was chief of the Biological Therapeutics Branch of the National Cancer Institute's

Ronald B. Herberman, MD

The first director of the University of Pittsburgh Cancer Institute (UPCI), Ronald B. Herberman, MD, is an internationally recognized tumor immunologist with a passion for translating laboratory research into better patient care. "Ron Herberman is very quiet," says Eugene N. Myers, MD, FACS. "But he's very effective. UPCI was nothing. Nobody. Didn't exist. Just on paper. All of sudden, there he came in from NIH. I don't know how he does it. Very quiet. Then bam!"

Biological Response Modifiers Program. Systematic and low-key, Herberman was recruited as the founding director of the Pittsburgh Cancer Institute in September 1985.

RONALD HERBERMAN: *I initially visited Pittsburgh only as a favor to my old friends Drs. Barbara and Gerald Levey. It was February, and I remember being so cold that I could hardly wait to leave. But then I came under the spell of Tom Detre. I became intrigued by his vision to organize a diverse array of existing faculty and to launch an aggressive effort to recruit additional faculty to develop a strong cancer center. I soon realized that this mandate would provide me with the opportunity to directly make a major impact on the clinical care of cancer patients, by not only leading a multidisciplinary cancer research program, but also promoting rapid translation to improve treatment, early detection, and prevention of cancer. This was an unusual, and irresistible, opportunity.*

"The man is made of titanium," Detre declares. "Not even steel. He knew what to do." With Detre's support and the accumulated war chest, Herberman immediately began working from a cramped, makeshift office to recruit researchers whose discoveries would translate into the most advanced clinical care of people with cancer. He claims his chief strength is "persistence."

In record time, the Cancer Institute by 1990 would become the youngest cancer center ever to receive the National Cancer Institute's most prestigious designation as a Comprehensive Cancer Center – the only cancer center in western Pennsylvania with this distinction. As the University of Pittsburgh Cancer Institute (UPCI), it would grow to include more than 625 research faculty members, and rank tenth in funding from the National Cancer Institute.

"UPCI helped to propel us into a whole new status in the world of academic health centers and medical schools," says internationally known surgeon Eugene N. Myers, MD, FACS, Distinguished Professor and Emeritus Chair, Department of Otolaryngology.

In a 1989 report to the Richard King Mellon Foundation, Detre would assess the results of his various programs:

> The very generous grants we have received … have had a dramatic catalytic effect on literally every aspect of our academic activities, clinical care, teaching, and research. Equal and perhaps even more important, however, is the change in "climate" it has brought about: for many years the prevailing view was that outstanding academicians would not come to Pittsburgh, and, thus, we would have to "settle" for faculty who were solidly competent but not brilliant. In our most recent wave of faculty recruitment, including several key chairmanships, we have had our choice among candidates who represent the top in their fields.

University of Pittsburgh School of Medicine Commencement, 1983. Thomas Detre, MD (left), and Nathan Stark (right), a health policy lawyer, who preceded Dr. Detre as vice chancellor for the Health Sciences from 1974 to 1984

New Powers

By 1984 Thomas Detre had become one of the most powerful and admired – and feared and resented – officials at the University of Pittsburgh. Rumors about "infighting" circulated when in May 1984 the dean of the School of Medicine, Donald Leon, MD, resigned, and Detre became interim dean. Many believed that Leon, who had opposed any plans for consolidating the Oakland hospitals, had been forced to quit.

THOMAS DETRE: *Forced? Leon was well liked by everybody. But I said to Posvar that I don't think he will be able to recruit and organize well enough to ensure the future of not just the medical school but also the medical center. He really doesn't understand what is needed, and he is resisting changes I want to make.*

Two months later the senior vice chancellor for the Health Sciences, Nathan Stark, also announced his departure, opening the door for Detre to succeed him. "The real story behind Nathan Stark's planned departure ... is the steady rise in power of his assistant, Dr. Thomas Detre, according to medical school faculty members," reported the *Pittsburgh Post-Gazette* in July 1984. Detre's detractors described him as "an overly ambitious man who has hurt the school by delaying necessary hiring in the medical school's basic sciences departments and creating too many new medical institutes such as the Pittsburgh Cancer Center."

But the chancellor again backed Detre. "The critics here are in a definite minority," Posvar told the newspaper. "The fundamental objective here is the achievement of excellence. The people who are critical are either those who fear excellence or who have something to lose from it, or those who misunderstand what we're doing." Detre said mildly that he found it "a little boring that people are always after the negative aspects of such stories."

A search committee headed by Department of Surgery Chair Henry Bahnson met to select a new senior vice chancellor for the Health Sciences. Within six weeks they made their recommendation: Thomas Detre. Posvar announced the appointment in November 1984, igniting an hour-long uproar in the university senate council. Members of the Tenure and Academic Freedom Committee demanded to know if outside candidates had been considered. "The university had the best candidate available in the country," Posvar countered. Dr. Jack E. Freeman, the university's vice chancellor for planning and budget, and not always a Detre fan, added that he "regards the nomination of Dr. Detre as simply an extraordinary statement of confidence in his ability."

One week after his appointment as senior vice president for the Health Sciences (Posvar changed the chancellor title to president in October 1984), Detre named Jeffrey A. Romoff associate vice president for the Health Sciences, his former position. A new era at the University of Pittsburgh had begun.

"My motto, as I often said, is that no department or school can be its own university. No department or school can accumulate the necessary expertise for all the things they need to do or would like to do. So they have to rely on the expertise of others."

— Thomas Detre, MD

Merger by Fiat

"Thomas Detre re-engineered the medical school field," states Scott Lammie, who began working with Detre and Romoff in the 1980s when he was a certified public accountant at Arthur Andersen and at Coopers & Lybrand in Pittsburgh. "Most medical schools are traditional, classical silos. To win all this cancer research and other NIH funding, he really needed to foster cross-expertise across departments."

Now with few limitations on his authority to recruit stronger department chairs and to promote collaboration among disciplines, Detre raised new hackles: He moved to consolidate several basic science departments. "The basic science researcher cannot be a lone ranger today," he said yet again. "They need interaction with their peers in related fields." Departmental autonomy, he said, "has to give way to an institutional planning process … implementing what are institutionally established priorities."

THOMAS DETRE: *No department or school should be its own university. That makes no sense. That's very parochial thinking. This whole territoriality characterizes mostly second-rate institutions. And it makes no sense because you don't want to create redundancies. You want to fill in gaps; and it doesn't matter where the gaps are being filled in as long as the campus itself provides a comprehensive matrix for the basic sciences.*

Western Pennsylvania's hilly terrain separates the University of Pittsburgh's Oakland campus (foreground) into the upper and lower campuses. The upper campus tends to signify the schools of the health sciences and the hospitals, while the lower campus is more the province of the arts and sciences. Dr. Detre urged collaboration between the two.

Posvar had urged Detre to undertake a merger of the departments of Microbiology, in the School of Medicine, and Biological Sciences, in the School of Arts and Sciences. At Pitt, however, there were cultural clashes between these "upper" and "lower" campuses. Reactions to the plan ranged "from dismay to public protest." Professors in the medical school feared heavier teaching loads and fewer tenured positions.

"My faculty was dead set against merging," remembers Julius Youngner, who chaired Microbiology, "and so was the faculty of the Department of Biological Sciences."

Disciplines Detre felt had suffered "catastrophic neglect" were molecular biology and genetics. He then suggested a merger between the departments of Microbiology and Biochemistry in the School of Medicine.

JULIUS YOUNGNER: *I didn't think it was a good idea. I thought that these were two disparate groups. So I said to Tom, "I'm going to resist." Tom said, "No, it's a good idea. Juli, Juli, try, try. I'm counting on you." And he had meetings, and we discussed and discussed this idea and came to no agreement.*

Then one day I was at a conference in Las Vegas, and somebody in Pittsburgh called me and said, "Oh, it's in the paper today."

"What?" I said.

"Your department has been merged with Biochemistry." And so Tom got his way. He realized he wasn't going to get agreement, so he did it by fiat.

Tom called me and said, "Are you going to be chairman of this [new department], or do you want me to appoint [someone else]?" So I saluted, and then I made a real effort. He wanted Molecular Biology in there because he felt this was the new thing. So we added the name. It was Microbiology, Biochemistry, and Molecular Biology – with a great abbreviation, MB^2.

When Youngner retired from the chairmanship in 1989, the department changed its name to Molecular Genetics and Biochemistry. Among other departments Detre would consolidate were Anatomy and Cell Biology (a merger of Physiology and Cell Biology) and the separate departments of Pharmacology at the School of Medicine and at the School of Pharmacy. He would create a Department of Human Genetics, an interface between the School of Medicine and the Graduate School of Public Health. He would remake the School of Health Related Professions into the School of Health and Rehabilitation Sciences and change its focus from entry-level professional education to research and advanced graduate study.

And, in addition to a new dean for the School of Medicine, Detre would recruit new chairs with outstanding academic credentials for the departments of Surgery, Pharmacology, Dermatology, Orthopedic Surgery, Diagnostic Radiology, Radiation Oncology, Clinical Epidemiology, and Pediatrics. Within two years of Richard L. Simmons' 1987 arrival as chair of Surgery, that department would rank among the top recipients of NIH grants and contracts among surgery departments in the nation. Thomas Starzl would describe Simmons as "the leading chairman in this country for the next dozen years."

THOMAS DETRE: *I always tried to be polite and considerate; but if a department chair had to be changed, I was not hesitant.*

Richard L. Simmons, MD, Distinguished Service Professor of Surgery and chair emeritus of the Department of Surgery

JULIUS YOUNGNER: *There was lots of opposition to Tom, lots. He felt that [no job] was permanent if [people] didn't meet the standards and goals that he set. He said to me, "Juli, Juli, nobody has a condominium here." [But] he never fired anybody. He had a way of gently moving them aside or making them realize that they were not welcome. He was very adamant in getting his way because he had a goal, and he was single-minded about it. At the same time, there was a compassion he had which people didn't see.*

Detre's goal was world-class patient care in Pittsburgh. "What is the best possible patient care we can offer?" he always urged his colleagues to ask. "How can we do the best we know how with what we know today?" Only through applied clinical and translational research, he believed, could care be improved rapidly.

DAVID KUPFER: *One of the ingenious things in this environment is that walls don't exist between departments, or between schools. What's interesting is that reduced the likelihood that there would then be walls between clinical issues and academic issues, clinical demands and research demands. If you reduce all of those barriers, then you – more rapidly, more quickly – have a chance of really going to the big game.*

"There was a lot of raw material here – gold – but it wasn't being put together."

— Thomas E. Starzl, MD, PhD

Integrating the university-related hospitals

1985 After unsuccessful attempts at negotiation between Eye & Ear Hospital and Presbyterian-University Hospital, Eye & Ear reorganizes its board membership to include two-thirds university-appointed trustees. A shared management arrangement is developed with the university, under the direction of the WPIC management team headed by Thomas Detre, MD, and Jeffrey A. Romoff.

1986 The boards of the University of Pittsburgh, Presbyterian-University Hospital, and Presbyterian-University Health System approve a Concept Paper outlining the creation of the Medical and Health Care Division (MHCD). The WPIC team now manages WPIC, Eye & Ear Hospital, and Presbyterian-University Hospital.

Thomas Detre, MD, is president of MHCD; Jeffrey A. Romoff is executive vice president.

Thomas Detre, MD

1990 The restructuring of The Montefiore Hospital Association of Western Pennsylvania is completed, resulting in the right of Presbyterian-University Health System, Inc. (the parent of Presbyterian-University Hospital) to appoint two-thirds of Montefiore's board as well as in a closer working relationship between Presbyterian-University Hospital and Montefiore Hospital.

The university board approves changing the name of the Medical and Health Care Division to the University of Pittsburgh Medical Center (UPMC).

The University of Pittsburgh Biomedical Science Tower is dedicated.

Health care expenditures in the U.S. are $717 billion. Health care costs are rising at double the rate of inflation.

Jeffrey A. Romoff

4

Consolidating

"I thought these hospitals eventually should merge into a single entity. I knew this was going to be a long and painstaking process. So we swallowed up little pieces one by one." — Thomas Detre, MD

Despite the remarkable achievement of building UPMC, few people really understand *why* Thomas Detre, Jeffrey A. Romoff, and their colleagues worked so hard to make this happen. Every strategy, every move, from re-engineering WPIC to creating a specialty hospital in Sicily, was in pursuit of the academic mission. "It was always a three-pronged approach," says Farrell Rubenstein, the international accounting firm executive who chaired the University of Pittsburgh Trustees' Committee on the Health Sciences: "academics, research, and clinical care; and the three were all tied to each other."

Oakland

"All these hospitals in this medical center were independent fiefdoms, controlled by very strong-minded administrators," said George A. Huber about the former University Health Center of Pittsburgh.

Chaos in Oakland

At WPIC, in order to drive their mission to create excellence, the Detre team had honed their ability to "stimulate, expropriate, and redirect clinical monies." Now, in 1984, with Detre as senior vice president of the Health Sciences at the University of Pittsburgh, he and his associates turned their attention to transforming a consortium of teaching hospitals into a first-class academic medical center – by transplanting the WPIC model.

First they needed to gain control of the university-related but independently run Oakland hospitals. "Tom Detre would talk about harnessing the power that he saw on this hill," recalls Robert Cindrich, who did legal work for WPIC. "He saw fragmentation. [The hospitals were] all separate but all highly dependent on the faculty and the university. And he saw the university as not getting a fair shake out of this."

"I have always viewed what we found here, whether it be WPIC or the University Health Center of Pittsburgh, as being underutilized and even wasted natural resources. Our driving force is an abiding belief that we can take these natural resources and do a much better job of mining them and making them work for us."

— Jeffrey A. Romoff

At that time the hospitals comprised what Romoff termed "the underutilized and even wasted natural resources" of the University Health Center of Pittsburgh (UHCP). Established in 1965, this was an "impotent" consortium with no power to govern or manage its members: Presbyterian-University, Eye & Ear, Montefiore, Children's, and Magee-Womens hospitals, along with WPIC and Falk Clinic.

Rubenstein described the situation as "chaos in Oakland."

THOMAS DETRE: *In the first place, let's talk about simple economics. It really was a waste of time that most members of the UHCP were independent entities … because they could exploit absolutely nothing synergistically. Every member of that UHCP board had veto power. And moreover, nobody understood what it was supposed to do. So I think it made perfect sense to move to a unified system. Across the river was Allegheny General, which had all of the departments that the various UHCP hospitals together had, but it was a unified system, because it was a single hospital.*

GEORGE TABER: *The hospital boards, although they wanted to cooperate, really were following the administrators' lead.*

"The UHCP hospitals represent a phenomenal fiscal resource," Detre wrote to Taber in 1983. "Their combined budgets approach $400 million annually." Detre also noted the hospitals' "unusually favorable geographic location." Presbyterian-University Hospital (Presby) and Eye & Ear Hospital occupied wings of the same building, across the street from WPIC and connected to Scaife Hall, home of the School of Medicine. Pedestrian bridges linked Children's and Falk Clinic to Presby. Montefiore, another large general medical and surgical hospital, was just a short distance away, and Magee-Womens not much farther.

At left, Presbyterian-University Hospital and Eye & Ear Hospital occupied wings of this same building. Eye & Ear Hospital was in the wing to the left, but by the mid-1980s it admitted fewer and fewer inpatients. Western Psychiatric Institute and Clinic (right) stands across the street.

PRESBYTERIAN-UNIVERSITY HOSPITAL

WESTERN PSYCHIATRIC INSTITUTE AND CLINIC

But to Detre, bricks and mortar did not an academic medical center make. He was scathing in his 1983 assessment of the hospitals' performance. "New buildings go up but the goal of providing highly specialized care usually available only in university hospitals is rarely met," he wrote at the time. "Some community hospitals do as well or better."

He was outraged that Presby had designed a radiology facility to share with Children's and Eye & Ear – without any input from the university. "Precisely because expert consultation was not sought," he fumed, "the [project] will not be able to accommodate NMR [nuclear magnetic resonance imaging], which will thus have to be built elsewhere at a much higher cost."

Particularly galling to Detre and Romoff was the fact that although the University of Pittsburgh School of Medicine paid the salaries of the full-time teaching faculty who also cared for patients, the hospitals gave back minimal support for medical education and research. Detre placed some of the blame on the university, which, in his opinion, "has not consistently provided assertive leadership geared to the development of world-class [hospitals]."

He threw down the gauntlet in a speech at Carnegie Mellon University in 1982. A university hospital had to be different from either a teaching hospital or a community hospital, he declared. "A university hospital's primary mandate is to be on the forefront of health training, research, and tertiary service delivery. Looking beyond the borders of its local area, it strives to be a trendsetter nationwide."

To Detre and Romoff the solution to "chaos in Oakland" was obvious.

The University of Pittsburgh – they, as leaders of the university's health sciences – would have to manage the hospitals where the university's teaching, research, and patient care took place. Others had been reluctant or unable to take on the hospitals. Detre and Romoff were not.

"There was virtually no control by the university over [these hospitals] until Detre."

— Hon. Robert J. Cindrich

Destruction Precedes Creation

The first step was to change the governance of the UHCP. With university trustee Farrell Rubenstein as an ally, Detre asked in March 1983 that university-managed WPIC formally replace the university as a voting member of UHCP. "The university is no longer to be regarded as one among others … but rather as a strong partner with each hospital," said Chancellor Posvar in a letter to faculty members.

Outsiders misinterpreted this move as a retreat; they assumed it meant the university was admitting that past attempts to unify the teaching hospitals had failed. "Apparently everyone is relieved," the *Pittsburgh Post-Gazette* wrote in an editorial. "The hospitals feel freed of a threatened centralized control with which they never felt comfortable."

Farrell Rubenstein, former chair of the University of Pittsburgh Committee on the Health Sciences

Relief would prove temporary. In 1983 the Detre/university team took back the management and governance of Falk Clinic from the UHCP. They made this move through the University of Pittsburgh Committee on the Health Sciences, which Rubenstein chaired and on which Detre served. The committee modified its membership to include all university appointees to the board of Presbyterian-University Hospital (the university at the time appointed one-third of Presby's board) as well as two community members nominated by the Presby board. The Committee on the Health Sciences then became the Board of Governors of Falk Clinic, in the same way that committee had taken over the governance of WPIC in 1970.

LOREN ROTH: *On the sixth floor of WPIC [the administrative floor] everybody was so excited. George Huber said, "Wow! Do you know today is the day we are going to manage Falk Clinic?" I thought they were out of their minds. Why would these people abandon WPIC? Why would they divert and diffuse their energies? I didn't get it.*

Later remodeled, the Falk Clinic opened in 1931 as an ambulatory care teaching facility. Thomas Detre, MD, and his University of Pittsburgh administrative team took over its management in 1983 — a move Jeffrey A. Romoff described as "mining underused resources."

JEFFREY A. ROMOFF: *We took on the management of Falk Clinic really in order to [develop better collaborations with the] full-time faculty of the university, whom the university only resented. [The university] didn't know how to use them, didn't know how to cultivate them, didn't know how to get any service out of them, didn't know how to get any academic excellence out of them.*

Subsequently, Eye & Ear Hospital would come under the same management, to escape the clutches of Presby.

Eye & Ear Hospital: My Enemy's Enemy Is My Friend

Even within the University of Pittsburgh, few understood Detre's vision of taking the independent UHCP hospitals and creating a great academic medical center. In the university, "Detre and I were a foreign body," Romoff asserts.

JEFFREY A. ROMOFF: *But Eye & Ear Hospital needed to get liberated, and we used the university to liberate Eye & Ear. We learned to make linkages. We didn't have this great long-term vision yet except academic excellence. But we then came up with a model that we invented, that made it safe for the university, for us, to use our parent the university without any risk to the university. No one wants to take risks. In everything we did, it was always we who took the risk.*

The Eye & Ear Hospital of Pittsburgh, founded in 1895, suffered when advances in cataract surgery made inpatient stays largely unnecessary.

One who did support this vision was George H. Taber, elected chairman of the board of trustees of Presbyterian-University Hospital in 1982. As a foundation and civic leader who cared deeply about strengthening the region's economy, he, too, wanted a unified academic medical center. A spare, reserved New Englander, Taber was the personification of speaking softly and carrying a big stick.

Of all the UHCP hospitals, Presby was king of Cardiac Hill. Thanks to Thomas Starzl's liver transplantation program and a revival of heart transplantation, "this is the hottest center for transplants in the world," Starzl told *The New York Times* in 1985. And Presby's then-president, who had a reputation for being imperious and contentious, made sure everybody knew it.

But Presby was running out of room … and the word was out that Starzl had received an offer to move his program to a university where he would have all the space and resources he needed. And there in Presby's west wing sat largely empty Eye & Ear Hospital. The Presby administration eyed it like a wolf stalking a stray lamb.

J. Wray Connolly, a leader of the Eye & Ear Hospital board, suggested to Dr. Detre that the university should take over the hospital.

"Eye & Ear Hospital by then had gotten into big trouble," explains Farrell Rubenstein, "primarily because the medical profession developed a way to deal with cataracts through laser surgery as opposed to your being in the hospital for two weeks with sandbags on each side of your head."

"Everything that the Eye & Ear Hospital did, certainly on the eye side, became ambulatory," Dr. Detre agrees. "They had 170 beds, and they didn't know what to do with them."

"The only thing really remaining in Eye & Ear was Gene Myers' work," recalls J. Wray Connolly, a leader of the Eye & Ear Hospital Board of Trustees. "Not that Dr. Myers' work wasn't important; it was critical," he adds.

Eugene N. Myers, MD, FACS, was one of the world's top experts in otolaryngology and head and neck surgery. Honors from universities and medical societies around the globe line his office walls. As chair of the Department of Otolaryngology at the University of Pittsburgh for thirty-three years, he had built it into "the best ENT [ear, nose and throat] department in the country," according to Dr. Detre. This star surgeon had no hesitation about standing up for the rights of his Eye & Ear Hospital colleagues and himself.

J. WRAY CONNOLLY: *Although the surgeons did not want to lose the operating-room priorities that they enjoyed, from an overall board and business standpoint, I think there was pretty clear unanimity that we could just not afford to keep that hospital. And our approach was to Presby because that seemed to make the most sense.*

FARRELL RUBENSTEIN: *They were in the same building, of course, where Presby is, and Presby was dying for space, and they went to Presby and said, "Buy us," and Presby said, "Yes." And the negotiations were awful. [The Presby president] was fighting over how much Eye & Ear would pay Presby to collect their receivables. For survival, Presby needed that space, and he's fighting with them over $50,000 essentially. And threatening to fire all their employees.*

Eugene N. Myers, MD, FACS, Distinguished Professor and emeritus chair, Department of Otolaryngology

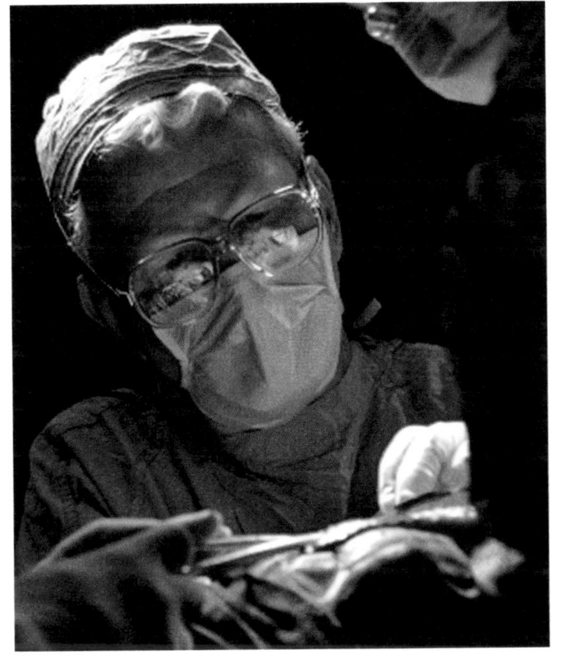

EUGENE MYERS: *At Eye & Ear there was always this free-floating anxiety about Presby. The old guard always feared that Presby would just eat them up one day. And so it looked as if the prophecy was coming true. The Presby administrator ... circled the castle kind of thing. He decided that if you just let [Eye & Ear] go on, they're going to go out of business, and they'll give you the hospital for nothing; so don't help them. You know, it's the old expression: "Just because you're paranoid doesn't mean they're not out to get you." But in the meantime, Starzl was on the uptake, and Presby didn't have any space.*

By 1985 the two hospitals appeared finally to have hammered out an agreement. But at the last minute, at a dinner at downtown Pittsburgh's stately Duquesne Club to announce the affiliation, the Eye & Ear board suddenly rejected the deal. They were fed up with their hospital being treated "like a stepchild" by Presby administration. George Taber and other board leaders seethed. "There we were sitting at dinner with nothing to do," he remembered. "There were no points to discuss!"

J. Wray Connolly, a lawyer who could be outspoken, tough, and intimidating – and who was used to being treated with deference – resented the way Presby's administration "rebuffed us by making offers that were absurdly low." He picked up the phone, made a surprise call to Thomas Detre, and requested a meeting. When he arrived at Detre's office in WPIC, Detre walked to the reception room to greet him, as he greeted all his visitors, with courtly charm. Connolly came straight to the point. The University of Pittsburgh, not Presbyterian-University Hospital, should take over Eye & Ear.

J. WRAY CONNOLLY: *My relationship with Dr. Detre was not a particularly close one at that time. I knew who he was. I respected him. I came to him largely because it seemed to be the only other place we could go. And I'll never forget the day he said to me – because the university didn't get along all that well with Presby either at that point – "My enemy's enemy is my friend." I've never forgotten that.*

Detre and Romoff were amazed and elated at the opportunity Connolly dangled in front of them ... but also aware of the hurdles between them and this prize. First they had to convince a skeptical University of Pittsburgh that there would be little risk in taking over Eye & Ear. And they had to placate their ally, George Taber, chairman of the Presby board, who was "furious" about the collapse of the two hospitals' agreement.

Farrell Rubenstein found himself caught in the crossfire.

FARRELL RUBENSTEIN: *Members of the Presby board were pretty mad. One day I was "accosted" on the street in front of the Duquesne Club by two of them. I tried to explain to them what happened, and I also said to them – which was true – "We at the university are not trying to buy Eye & Ear Hospital to hurt Presby. We are trying to help you."*

"Actually, Mr. Taber was mad at me," Detre recollects.

"Well, everyone on the Presby side was a little cross with you," George Taber retorted good-naturedly.

Myers was equally dismayed. "All of a sudden I saw my whole career, my department and everything disappearing," he remarks. "That loss of autonomy was threatening."

Convincing the risk-averse University of Pittsburgh to buy a hospital and allow the WPIC management team to run it seemed even more of a challenge than pacifying the trustees and doctors. George Huber, WPIC's smart, affable legal counsel, was assigned to write a contract all sides could buy into. "Organizational structure was always something I was interested in," he says. "I remember trying to think about how we could relate to one another. As I recall, I was thinking about it one day in the shower, and I came up with the thought of how it could be done."

Like most good ideas, what Huber proposed seemed simple and transparent: a shared governance and management model, with equal university and community representation and stronger faculty input into planning and decision making. Reorganize the Eye & Ear governing board and enter into a contract for management of the hospital by the university/WPIC, just as the Commonwealth of Pennsylvania had transferred the management of WPIC to the university in 1949.

"Everything we did was on the face of it disruptive to the status quo — and was treated as such. No one wants the challenge of excellence because it's uncomfortable. It is just uncomfortable."

— Jeffrey A. Romoff

GEORGE HUBER: *This was kind of like a leveraged buyout. It didn't have to be an asset purchase; it didn't have to be a merger; it didn't have to be a consolidation. What we said to the board of Eye & Ear Hospital was let us – the university – come in and control the board, and let us provide the management of Eye & Ear Hospital. We could institute better reimbursement methodologies and better facilities management; we could eliminate overhead; we could bring them into our purchasing programs and into our financial systems, and all our other economies of scale, and reduce the costs.*

FARRELL RUBENSTEIN: *It was ingenious. It was a brilliant move. We agreed, within the university, that we would write a check as soon as we got that control from the Eye & Ear Hospital for $10 million to the Eye & Ear Foundation, which they had set up to engender research.*

GEORGE HUBER: *Which was very important. That money was given to the foundation with the thought that whatever the foundation generated from investments would come back to support academic medicine in the departments of Otolaryngology and Ophthalmology.*

Within weeks Detre had brokered an agreement. Myers was soon satisfied that he would have the operating room access he needed for his complex, lengthy surgeries involving head and neck cancer, and that his department would continue to grow. The only sticking point was the university's top officers. The "ultraconservative" executive vice president, Jack E. Freeman, was reluctant to commit the university. "He just wouldn't give them the guarantee," Rubenstein recalls. "I remember Jeff was just going through the ceiling. Finally we got him to write a letter."

On July 26, 1985, Freeman signed, in Chancellor Posvar's absence, a rather noncommittal letter assuring Eye & Ear of the university's "best efforts to assist the hospital in fulfilling its payment obligation." He also named the four university appointees to the new, six-person board: Thomas Detre, Farrell Rubenstein, Wesley Posvar, and Jack E. Freeman.

EUGENE MYERS: *So instead of going down into the black hole, all of a sudden we went up into infinity, really limited only by our imagination. We were rescued!*

With $5 and a lot of gumption, Dr. Louise Wotring Lyle opened the five-room Presbyterian Hospital in Allegheny City, Pittsburgh's North Side, in 1893. In 1910 the hospital moved into a modern new building (left), but when the trustees faced financial problems in the 1920s, they gratefully accepted Pitt's offer to relocate to Oakland.

Presbyterian-University Hospital and the Magna Carta of UPMC

Detre and his team now managed the clinical revenues of WPIC, Falk Clinic, and Eye & Ear Hospital. Rising amid these three was Presbyterian-University Hospital, the major inpatient setting for the School of Medicine faculty. To build a great academic medical center, Presby was the flagship they had to have.

GEORGE HUBER: *We saw Eye & Ear as a wonderful opportunity to leverage integration. If we control Eye & Ear, we thought, we have blocked Presby's opportunity to expand. They don't have another wing they can move into. They are landlocked. We thought this may, this* may *just have Presby come to us and see whether or not there might be some accommodation.*

Presbyterian Hospital had opened in 1893 on Pittsburgh's North Side. In 1927, low on funds, the Presby board gratefully accepted the University of Pittsburgh's offer of land on which to establish a new hospital in Oakland. This new building opened in 1938. But before Thomas Starzl moved his liver transplant program to Pittsburgh in 1981, Presby was in some trouble.

THOMAS STARZL: *When I came, the hospital had a low occupancy. It was losing the battle with Allegheny General, which had become the dominant hospital here in the city, partly because, I think, of a decision by Hank Bahnson not to emphasize adult heart surgery. So the coronary artery surgery was going across town, and the hospital wasn't fully occupied. It was very sleepy – then we arrived, and suddenly we filled the whole damned hospital up.*

"The relationship between Presby and the university was contentious, and that's putting it mildly," says Farrell Rubenstein. "Presby was reinvesting very little of the money it made [back into] the medical school, and [the university] didn't know how to deal with it."

This lack of commitment to research and education was the antithesis of everything Detre and Romoff believed in. They were also contemptuous of what they saw as Presbyterian's "appeasement" of the insurers. By not maximizing reimbursement, they felt, the hospital disadvantaged both the university and the community.

GEORGE HUBER: *That was a key issue. [Presby's] thought was that they would look good to Blue Cross of Western Pennsylvania, which was also the intermediary for Medicare, if they could reduce to its bare bones what reimbursement Presby would receive. Meanwhile the rest of the world was maximizing third-party reimbursement for graduate medical education in order to use those dollars to support medical schools, medical school faculty, and recruitment.*

"They said they were not going to try to get their medical education reimbursement from Medicare because Presbyterian-University Hospital is a 'community' hospital," disparages Detre. "'Ahhhh,' we thought. That was very kind of them to do that. Because Mr. Taber and several board members then entered that discussion."

George Huber remembers, "We started to do an analysis which showed what the Presby administration had truly given away. I don't think we thought that the administration was communicating to the board to the extent that they should have been about how they may have disadvantaged the hospital (as well as the university)."

Thomas Detre always urged his colleagues to ask, "What is the best possible patient care we can offer? How can we do the best we know how with what we know today?"

Robert Cindrich remembers that in 1985, "Jeffrey Romoff was the 'tough guy' given the task of taking on the deficiencies of the management of Presby." Forceful, compelling, persuasive, and above all prepared as a speaker, Romoff presented the university's argument to officers of the Presbyterian-University Hospital board. He said, George Huber recollects, "You have an administrator here who's really not doing what's in the best interests of your hospital or of the university. That's why you have mediocre academic programs. You're not generating the kind of income that you could generate, to recruit outstanding faculty not only to teach but also to do research and all the things an academic medical center ought to be doing. You're starving the university, and that's wrong!"

Over the summer of 1985 Detre talked with George Taber, Presby's chair, about how his university-employed team could manage the hospital. In September Taber spoke to the board about the need "to unite the leadership of our medical center and achieve the full potential of that opportunity."

Board response was mixed. Some members were antagonistic, fearing loss of autonomy. Some were merely skeptical. Many mistrusted Detre's motives and power, as well as his reputation for autocracy. Robert C. Todd Jr., then a senior vice president of Pittsburgh National Bank who served as vice chair of the Presbyterian board, probably represented the majority feeling: "I was concerned that maybe we wouldn't be able to be as independent or as strong financially as we had been."

In October Taber asked Detre to prepare a white paper outlining his philosophy and the advantages of integration. Jeffrey A. Romoff has characterized this document, the Concept Paper approved in June 1986, as "the most fascinating thing, the most important thing we probably ever did."

To communicate their agenda to the Presby board and solicit the board's ideas and cooperation, Detre, Romoff, and Huber met with each of the twenty-nine Presby trustees. Usually the meetings took place in Detre's WPIC office, furnished in modern leather and chrome. A luncheon would be served on a travertine coffee table that could be raised or lowered at the push of a button. On one memorable occasion this electronic table malfunctioned, spilling a board member's lunch into her lap. Generally, though, Huber remembers that "Dr. Detre, who is just so gracious and so intelligent and so charming and so alluring – he just handled those meetings beautifully. Mr. Taber did a marvelous job of asking questions and stimulating discussion."

THOMAS DETRE: *Basically, we wanted to tell the board that Presby had a chance to be a greater hospital. It would assume the identity of a university hospital – that doesn't mean that it wouldn't serve the community. But it could develop in areas that other hospitals couldn't, because they wouldn't have the scientific knowledge. We talked really about a symbiosis between science and the practice of medicine. This was a little more difficult at the time, because the medical school was not yet much of a research establishment. So what we sent to the board was a promissory note, that we could develop a greater medical center.*

ROBERT TODD: *A vision of becoming a great medical center was the kind of thing [our administration] had never really contemplated. I think that we were prepared to be led in that direction. I think that we were interested in seeing – I don't mean it from just a prestige point of view – but I think we were interested in taking leadership roles in certain areas. Then we did start to have the vision.*

THOMAS DETRE, MD, AND GEORGE H. TABER

Thomas Detre, MD, and George H. Taber, who chaired UPMC's board for eighteen years, worked closely to build one of America's leading academic medical centers.

George Huber wrote the first draft of the Concept Paper over the December 1985 holidays. Jeffrey A. Romoff wrote the introduction. Lawyer Alexander J. Ciocca summarized the board members' comments. George H. Taber, Robert C. Todd Jr., and Farrell Rubenstein reviewed it – while fielding "minor revolts."

GEORGE TABER: *Certain physicians heard what we were doing, and they would come plead with me or go and plead with Dr. Posvar. Chairmen of departments would go to the board members and sow seeds of doubt in their minds, and they had to be re-educated all over again. It was fun, actually! It doesn't sound like it, but it was.*

There were angry confrontations with the Presby administration – "just about a shoot-out at the OK Corral." In May 1986 Presby's president resigned.

The 1986 Concept Paper is essentially UPMC's Magna Carta. "As it was in 1930," the document states, "the future of Eye & Ear Hospital, Falk Clinic, Presbyterian-University Hospital, and the School of Medicine appear to be inextricably linked."

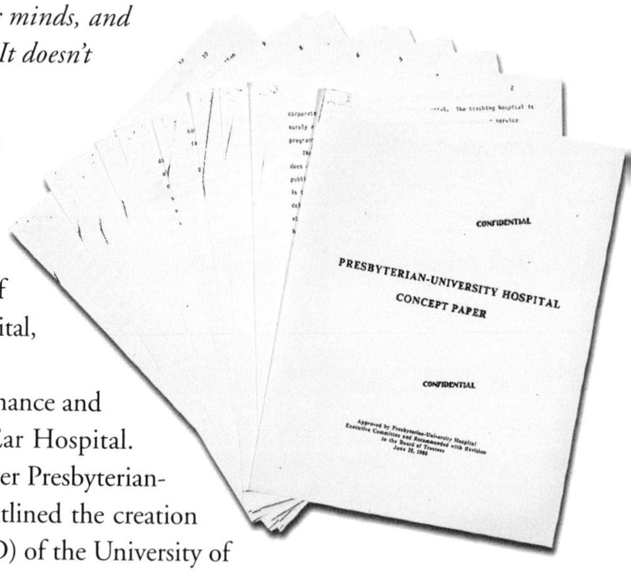

The foundation of the Concept Paper was the shared governance and management contract model Huber had crafted for Eye & Ear Hospital. The university would now appoint half the twenty-four-member Presbyterian-University Hospital board, rather than one-third. The plan outlined the creation of a new entity, the Medical and Health Care Division (MHCD) of the University of Pittsburgh. The division, with Detre as president and Romoff as executive vice president, would operate and manage the fiscal and clinical aspects of Pitt's School of Medicine, WPIC, Falk Clinic, and Presbyterian-University Hospital (into which Eye & Ear Hospital would be merged). As the university's senior vice president for the Health Sciences, Detre would continue to be responsible for all academic matters of the School of Medicine and MHCD, as well as other schools of the health sciences.

In July 1986 the model was adopted. The University of Pittsburgh, through the MHCD management contract and through the appointment of the hospitals' governing body, now had more authority over the university-related hospitals than ever in its history. The MHCD managers, led by Detre and Romoff, now controlled a significant moneymaker.

"Inherently," summarizes Romoff, "we emerged as a third party and filled the vacuum between them all."

CONFIDENTIAL

PRESBYTERIAN-UNIVERSITY HOSPITAL
CONCEPT PAPER

CONFIDENTIAL

"The most fascinating thing, the most important thing we probably ever did" is how Jeffrey A. Romoff has described the Concept Paper (above, and excerpt at right) developed by him, George A. Huber, and others in 1986. Their strategy united Presbyterian-University Hospital and the University of Pittsburgh through a shared governance and management model.

PRESBYTERIAN-UNIVERSITY HOSPITAL

CONCEPT PAPER

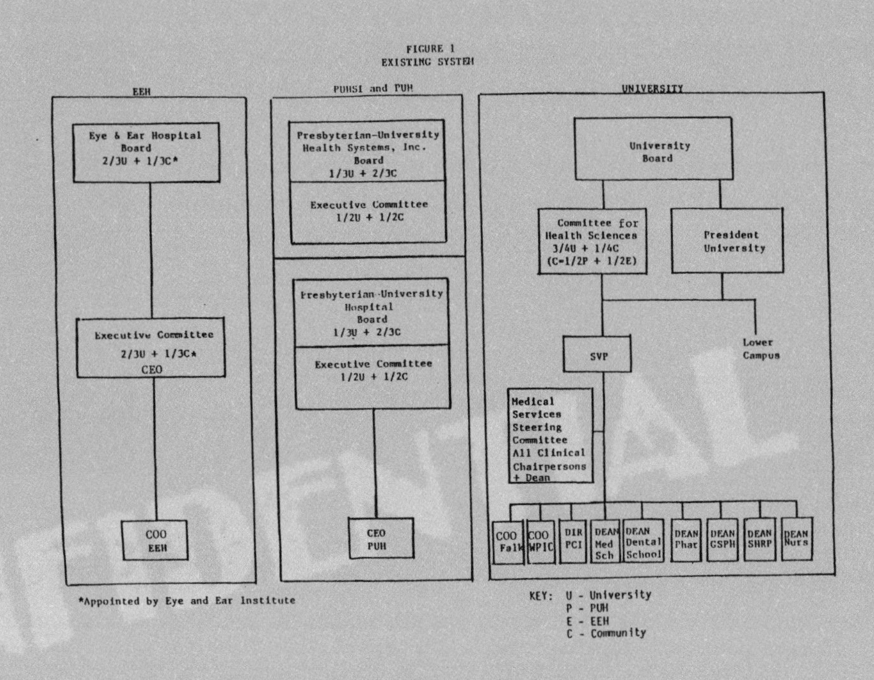

FIGURE 1
EXISTING SYSTEM

FIGURE 2
SHARED GOVERNANCE AND MANAGEMENT MODEL

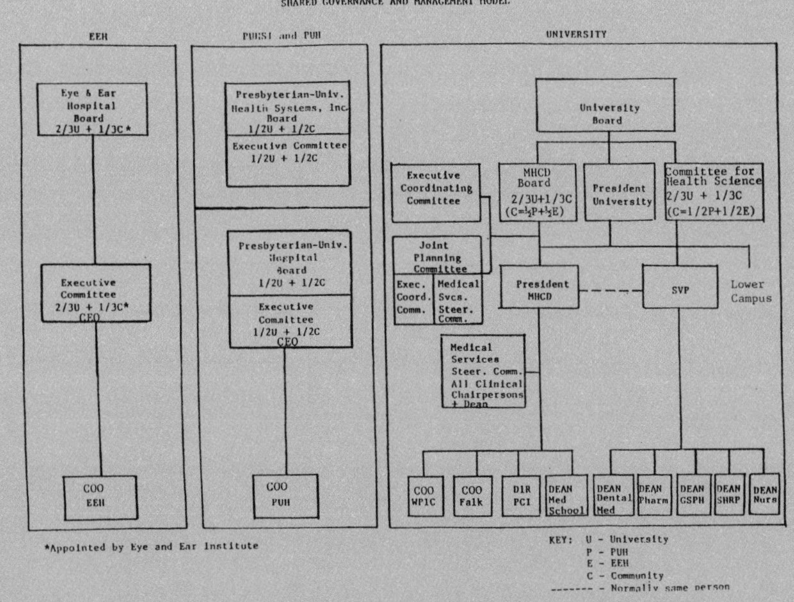

Integrating

The MHCD managers immediately began to integrate the new system, economically and operationally. Executive Vice President John Paul and his finance staff worked feverishly to put in needed financial controls, to work on a feasibility study for a $186 million bond issue to expand Presbyterian, and to integrate the management of this hospital and WPIC. David M. Farner, who would become senior vice president, UPMC, and chief of staff, Office of the President, UPMC, was at the time "a twenty-three-year-old kid" who had worked as an accountant and auditor at both Arthur Andersen and at Presbyterian-University Hospital, but had found the Presby culture "not all that challenging or stimulating," he remembers. "Then the Western Psych team came in, and it was like, how do you think higher than you can even imagine getting to?"

The finance team holed up on the windowless top floor of a former Isaly's deli and dairy building, working seven days a week until eleven o'clock at night to unearth every opportunity to improve Presbyterian's revenues.

Executive Vice President John Paul worked zealously for nearly thirty years to help build UPMC.

DAVID FARNER: *I went home to Buffalo for Christmas Eve, and just as we were sitting down to dinner, I got a call from John Paul asking me a question about the feasibility study.*

I drove back to Pittsburgh on Christmas Day. And we just kept working on it, and we kept digging. We had a successful business; how could it be more successful?

John Paul was charismatic. He was a leader that people were naturally drawn to. He understood the business of health care and its financing better than anybody else. Both he and Jeffrey Romoff are eloquent speakers and tireless workers. They both had a drive for perfection and for success.

Scott Lammie, a forensic accountant who has held a variety of key leadership jobs at UPMC, remembers the challenges.

SCOTT LAMMIE: *How do we pull all this together, drive integration, create standard platforms that are scalable to support the larger enterprise? Most of it at that time was solidifying the academic core, economically integrating programs ... and organizations, and then, more importantly, operationally integrating them and creating technology to support the enterprise. I remember when we put the first local area network into Western Psych. This was the beginning of the evolution of the information technology age, which would serve as the engine to drive our growth and success.*

These integration efforts provided more than $225 million to invest in the expansion of the transplantation program, the cancer institute, and other research initiatives.

Montefiore Hospital

While Presby began to blossom in the late 1980s, another nearby competitor was cast into its shadow. This was Montefiore Hospital, opened in 1908 to serve Pittsburgh's Jewish community and to assure Jewish physicians, in that restrictive era, of a place to practice medicine. Montefiore had moved from the Hill District into its new building near the university in 1929. But not until 1969 did it join the UHCP. Farrell Rubenstein says that "Montefiore ... loved the university until they got too close to the university. Then they didn't love the university anymore, and they got contentious with the university. They'd get a program, they loved the university. They wanted a program they didn't get, they'd hate the university. So it was a roller-coaster relationship."

Montefiore wanted Presbyterian-University Hospital and the School of Medicine to share more clinical programs. But Detre took the position that Montefiore's programs were competitive and redundant, and that the hospital no longer had cultural reasons for existing as a separate institution. Business executive and investor Robert A. Paul, who chaired Montefiore's board from 1982 to 1985, agreed. He remembers that "it was quite obvious, at least to us, that the future of Montefiore as a freestanding hospital was not consistent with the original objectives of Montefiore. Clearly times had changed."

To sort out such issues, hospital and university leaders met in Dr. Detre's WPIC office on a Saturday morning in September 1989. Present were prominent real estate developer Stanley Gumberg, chairman of the Montefiore board; insurance executive William Lieberman, Montefiore's vice chair; Daniel Kane, president of the hospital; George Bernier Jr., MD, dean of the School of Medicine; Farrell Rubenstein, chair of the university's Committee on the Health Sciences; John Paul; Thomas Detre, MD; and Jeffrey A. Romoff.

"The hospitals were all separate but all highly dependent on the faculty and the university. And Tom Detre saw the university as not getting a fair shake out of this."

— Hon. Robert J. Cindrich

FARRELL RUBENSTEIN: *Ostensibly, at least at the beginning, it was a candid meeting, and certainly they understood that Presby was the flagship hospital, and whatever we could give to Presby, we were going to give to Presby, and if there was stuff left over, Montefiore would get it, and maybe one or two things in which they were highly specialized; but, on balance, Presby was the favorite child. Somewhere in the middle of the meeting, Stanley Gumberg blurted out, "Why don't you buy Montefiore?"*

Negotiations between the university and the hospital began ... and went on for months. "There were many doctors that did not want this to occur," recalls Robert Paul. "[But] we felt it was good for all concerned to be part of the larger program."

The Hebrew Ladies Hospital Aid Society was the force behind Pittsburgh's Montefiore Hospital (above), opened in 1908 to care for Jewish patients and to welcome Jewish physicians.

By the 1980s, the modern Montefiore Hospital (left) could look back on a distinguished history of medical advances and service to western Pennsylvania.

Montefiore became a part of Presbyterian-University Hospital in 1990 for the sum of $150 million, which included assets and the assumption of debt. The system gained the right to appoint two-thirds of Montefiore's board and to manage the hospital. The money for such a major investment would come from the clinical income of the hospitals the system already managed – WPIC, Eye & Ear, and Presby – as well as from a bond issue.

FARRELL RUBENSTEIN: *It was similar to Eye & Ear in that they ceded control of governance and the administrative operation of the hospital to [the university].*

DAVID FARNER: *The Montefiore board wanted the money to create a foundation. And they wanted the Ladies Hospital Aid Society, which had originally created Montefiore, to thrive.*

ROBERT PAUL: *It was really a thoughtful process. They were going to preserve the Montefiore tradition by funding a foundation.*

The purchase provided the funds to create the Jewish Healthcare Foundation, whose first board was the Montefiore Hospital board. Based on Jewish values and ideals as expressed through acts of social justice and charitable giving, the foundation has led innovative, substantive initiatives to improve health care in western Pennsylvania.

Interestingly, one of the hospital's assets was a share in HealthAmerica, the large health maintenance organization. Montefiore had a 20 percent stake in the $10 million purchase price when it and Coventry Corporation of Nashville, Tennessee, bought HealthAmerica Pennsylvania in 1988. The hospital had also signed a ten-year agreement with HealthAmerica making Montefiore the insurer's exclusive provider of patient services. But when Montefiore was merged into Presbyterian, Coventry terminated that agreement – "precipitously, thereby excluding us," John Paul would argue in 1995.

GEORGE HUBER: *And [then] HealthAmerica came to us and said, "Look, why don't you give us that share back?"*

Montefiore Hospital nurses promote a fundraising event for the Ladies Hospital Aid Society, ca. 1960.

DAVID FARNER: *They offered to take back the ownership, so we wouldn't have any more "responsibility" for it.*

GEORGE HUBER: *"What do you mean, give it back?" we said.*

DAVID FARNER: *Our demand to them was $100 million. They came to Pittsburgh for settlement talks. In the morning they were offering us $15 million. By one or two o'clock they were up to $48 million. We thought if we can get it to $50 million, we would have a deal.*

GEORGE HUBER: *This was on a Friday. By Monday morning they had wired us $50 million.*

"We Have Maximized the Synergism"

In 1990 the University of Pittsburgh Board of Trustees approved changing the name of the Medical and Health Care Division to the University of Pittsburgh Medical Center (UPMC).

"With your help," Dr. Detre wrote to George Taber on June 19, 1990, "and that of Mr. Farrell Rubenstein, we have successfully maximized the potential synergism that exists among the various entities managed by the Medical and Health Care Division and the six health science schools. The coming together of Presbyterian-University Hospital and Montefiore University Hospital removed what had been the final barrier to laying down the foundations of UPMC."

"They were an interesting pair – formidable because of the things they had accomplished, their clear ambitions to accomplish even more, and the force of their personalities – and then also interesting because they presented themselves in such different ways."

— Mark A. Nordenberg

Against significant opposition, Jeffrey A. Romoff becomes president of UPMC.

1992 Thomas Detre, MD, retires as president of UPMC; he remains senior vice chancellor for the Health Sciences at the University of Pittsburgh until 1998.

University of Pittsburgh Chancellor J. Dennis O'Connor, PhD, names Jeffrey A. Romoff senior vice chancellor for health administration and president of UPMC.

1995 Thanks to Dr. Detre's efforts to foster the rapid growth of medical research and to recruit some of the world's leading biomedical scientists, Pitt's share of funds awarded by the National Institutes of Health (NIH) between 1985 and 1995 has almost tripled.

1997 The University of Pittsburgh ranks in the top ten among academic institutions and their affiliates in funding from the NIH, a universally recognized benchmark of research excellence.

Jeffrey A. Romoff and Thomas Detre, MD

5

Transitions

"Being great is about the only way I like to see UPMC." — Jeffrey A. Romoff

To the extent that organizations accrete cultures, and to the extent that they reflect the individuality of their leaders, UPMC resonates with the personalities and values of its two chief architects, Thomas Detre and Jeffrey A. Romoff. "They were an interesting pair," observes Mark A. Nordenberg, who became chancellor of the University of Pittsburgh in 1996.

MARK NORDENBERG: *Formidable, because of the things they had accomplished, their clear ambitions to accomplish even more, and the force of their personalities – and then also interesting because they presented themselves in such different ways, with Tom being the more cosmopolitan European and Jeff being the kind of tough-minded, straight-ahead New Yorker, or, more particularly, product of the Bronx.*

THOMAS STARZL: *I think they were superb administrators, and I think they had a clear vision. Without them I couldn't possibly have done what were my objectives in life. Jeff is unlike almost anyone I've ever known in that he has very unusual intelligence, different, very abnormal. Maybe "unique" would be a better word.*

"Jeff is a little like a cross between Prospero and Zeus," states Mark L. Zeidel, MD, former chair of Medicine at the University of Pittsburgh. "Prospero because he kind of creates things, you know, ideas that become very powerful economic instruments; and Zeus because every once in a while he throws some thunderbolts."

Romoff, a generation younger than his mentor, rose to lead and transform UPMC in the 1990s. Somewhat of a mystery in Pittsburgh (by his own choosing), he has been described as brilliant, arrogant, inspiring, spellbinding, feared, and even ruthless.

He finds the last adjective misleading. "I don't resonate with 'ruthless,'" he says. "I do resonate with 'driven.' I resonate with 'purposeful.' I resonate with 'aggressive.' But 'ruthless' seems to be a violation of my inner sense of values. I actually think you can eradicate evil or incompetence and not be ruthless. It gets back to my sense of inner integrity."

The late Ralph J. Cappy, former Pennsylvania Supreme Court Chief Justice and first vice chairperson of the UPMC Board of Directors, stated, "In my twenty years of experience with Jeff Romoff, I have never seen him ever break his word." Leo W. Yochum, retired senior executive vice president of finance at Westinghouse Electric Corporation, agrees that Romoff is a man of impeccable integrity. But, he adds, "In the community that I traveled in, you tell anybody you sat on Presby's board, and the first name that came up was Romoff's. They said cruel things about him. His personality is a dominant one, and yet he is probably as shy a man as there ever was, in my opinion."

"He can visualize four moves down the game board when most people are lucky to get past the first one, and he has a thought-out plan for each one of those moves," observes Marshall W. Webster, MD, executive vice president, UPMC; president, Physicians Services Division; and chief medical officer, UPMC.

Former Pennsylvania Supreme Court Chief Justice Ralph J. Cappy chaired the University of Pittsburgh Board of Trustees from 2003 until his death in 2009.

"There is nobody better at strategizing," agreed Ralph Cappy, who at his death in 2009 chaired the University of Pittsburgh Board of Trustees. "He gets UPMC rolling down roads very early, anticipating where the industry is going to be."

MARK NORDENBERG: *Jeff has a wonderful set of human values that do not always emerge through what can be a brusque, aggressive style unless you've known him for a while. But he and I, over the course of the years, have had occasion to talk about a lot of different things, things that aren't limited to even human health, as broad as that is; and he is a human being who cares about people, and would like to be known as someone who did good for people.*

RALPH CAPPY: *I genuinely believe that Jeff Romoff has not been given the credit he is due for what he has done for this community. It goes to a commitment to helping this region survive.*

Romoff claims not to care about recognition. He cares only, he says, about building a great academic medical center and pushing it incessantly forward, never for a moment settling for the status quo. "The status quo, at least in my experience, is always inadequate," he states. "And worse than inadequate in health care, it's also harmful." He is powerfully, even passionately committed to leading and safeguarding a financially successful, integrated delivery system that can provide the best health care available anywhere in the world. He defines that care as the synthesis of clinical excellence, academic excellence, and community responsiveness.

Romoff reads avidly and widely – newspapers, histories, the latest academic medical journals. "You wonder what I did for *fun* – I used to love to talk to Bernie Fisher, I loved to talk to Tom Starzl, I love to talk to bright people about what they do," he reveals.

JEFFREY A. ROMOFF: *Yesterday I was with a young scientist who is doing something on ovarian cancer, and I listened to her ideas. I see her enthusiasm, and I see she wants to bring down the barriers of dominant paradigms, which is an overriding belief that I have. And you know, when I talk to her, I have this true sense of exhilaration.*

In conversation Romoff speedily sizes up a colleague's (or opponent's) strengths and weaknesses. He speaks two languages (English and Italian) but employs little if any small talk. In sports-obsessed Pittsburgh, he neither plays golf nor follows the professional teams, and he acknowledges that "I don't know how to make a judgment about a guy's personality based on how he reacts to three-putting a green." He can be exceptionally polite, giving an individual or a discussion his full attention and only in the rarest instances allowing a phone call to interrupt a meeting. He is admiring of and eager to praise his colleagues – and equally frank about sub-par performance. "I've never been shy about telling anybody what I think," he readily admits. Although friends say he has mellowed, all agree that he doesn't suffer fools gladly.

To a surprising extent he remains true to ideals of the 1960s. "I view myself as coming up *against* whatever I see that is not working well, or that is actually bad," he muses. "I see myself on a bit of a crusade. You know, my politics have always been kind of left of center. So [I see UPMC] as doing good works because it has good values."

But, he clarifies, "As important as it is for me to be doing good works, it is almost more important for me to do whatever I'm doing well. The moral fabric of this organization is not the result of the *output* of this organization. If an organization is to be effective, it needs to have a sense of inner integrity."

Romoff is an accomplished, effective, and quick-witted performer. He uses his resonant voice like a musical instrument. A trumpet player and one-time bandleader, the son and nephew of musicians, he speaks in extended riffs, the words rising to an agitated crescendo and falling to an edgy diminuendo. His accent remains pure Bronx: If he speaks of "drawing a gun," it comes out as "drawering a gun."

He can capture the imagination of an auditorium full of angry physicians with an intense, fact-filled speech about UPMC strategy. He also laughs often, sometimes at himself. Memories of his childhood sweetheart and first wife, Vivian, who died in 1983, can bring him to tears, as can thoughts of the "artistic vision" and integrity of UPMC.

JEFFREY A. ROMOFF

Named president of UPMC in 1992, Romoff has been described as brilliant, arrogant, inspiring, rapacious, spellbinding, feared, and even ruthless. He says he finds the last adjective misleading.

Romoff the Leader

UPMC's ascendance has caused Jeffrey A. Romoff to think more philosophically about managerial leadership, and about the effect of Thomas Detre's and his values on an organization that now impacts countless lives in several parts of the world. Leadership, he believes, has three components: integrity, the ability to synthesize, and the ability to leverage that synthesis.

JEFFREY A. ROMOFF: *Look, I've always been a powerful leader. I've always sought to lead. I'm not shy about that. But my self-awareness of the role of leadership was not as keen as it is now.*

So first I think the leader has to have a set of values, and has to implement major decisions in keeping with those values, that are reasonably transparent and that are something people can respect.

The second thing I think is vital about leadership – it relates to conducting an orchestra – is that great leaders of great organizations put pieces together. A great leader is constantly seeking to come up with new orchestrations, new combinations. And in hindsight, what UPMC has done brilliantly from the early times when Detre created centers (which were really putting pieces together and which were radical then) and what UPMC seeks to do today, is inspire people and institutions to collaborate – to combine in the orchestra in a way that all the major players feel productive and satisfied.

Then once you have a moral compass and you are putting the pieces together, then you're in a position to do what UPMC also does absolutely splendidly, which is that it leverages. It has created something greater than the sum of its parts by putting the pieces together. You can't with a single violin play a symphony. I mean, what is a symphony? It is the leveraging of each of the players into something that is greater than each of the players individually.

So this is the UPMC that I live in. This is the UPMC that never feels static. I wish I could come up with a better word than "feel," but that's what it is. There's no way to resonate with a soul unless you can feel it. You can't think it only. Dear God, I do a lot of thinking. But for the organization to vibrate, for the organization to resonate, for the organization to sound like an orchestra, it has to have a feel to it. That's when the inner music pulsates through an organization.

You may think this is hyperbole, which, in part, it is; that's the way I am. But [leadership is] a matter of creating a tone, of showing that we want the expression of excellence, that we want new ideas, and it's safe to have them, and it's pleasing to [carry] them [out].

The "Evil Empire" Holds Its Ground

Back in 1991, if Jeffrey A. Romoff had talked in this vein about the fledgling UPMC and its handful of Oakland hospitals, he might have been dismissed as a deluded Don Quixote. But even then the Pittsburgh media already sniped at the size and power of the "Pitt medical beast." UPMC's financial success and aggressive, impatient, corporate-style management raised hackles throughout the university and beyond.

Pitt's less well-funded schools looked on longingly when annual research support for the health sciences grew from $67 million in 1986 to over $100 million in 1991. The University of Pittsburgh became one of the fastest-growing research institutions in the country, thanks largely to Dr. Detre's successes in recruiting outstanding physicians and scientists and developing multidisciplinary centers of excellence. The School of Medicine gained twenty new endowed chairs between 1990 and 1993.

University of Pittsburgh Chancellor Mark A. Nordenberg and Jeffrey A. Romoff in 2004

"It was an interesting time, in terms of faculty reactions," recalls Chancellor Nordenberg. "There were those ... who always were envious of the medical school faculty, believing that they were advantaged in a broad range of ways including compensation and status."

Detre and Romoff were cast as power-hungry empire builders, but in retrospect, it's hard to tell what may have aggravated people more, their personalities or their success. Pittsburgh was a conservative place, often insular and resistant to change. The steel industry had created wide gaps between workers and management and enduring bitterness against big business, even when steel no longer dominated the economy. Western Pennsylvania's hills, valleys, and rivers formed natural barriers that some residents only rarely crossed. Churches and ethnic groups created cultural boundaries that kept people in check. And now here were these outsiders coming in and telling western Pennsylvanians how to run their hospitals and remake their economy, driving them to move beyond the bounds of their comfort zones, encouraging diversity and difference ... and making little effort to disguise their contempt for parochialism or mediocrity.

Even before J. Dennis O'Connor, PhD, succeeded Wesley Posvar as University of Pittsburgh chancellor in 1991, he had been warned about the "evil empire" on the upper campus. As O'Connor remembers, "There weren't too many people who didn't have an opinion about the health center and [what they called] this 'mad Hungarian,' 'the living personification of Lucifer himself,' or 'Dr. Detre and his hired guns.' I think there was a lot of academic jealousy about the health center."

Dennis O'Connor's "mandate was to get rid of Detre and me," Romoff asserts.

JEFFREY A. ROMOFF: *I think [this mandate] was from, as I believe Nietzsche called them, the gregarious desideratum. It's a wonderful expression. People like to be with other people who want the same thing. These are the people that are the audience of the world. These are the people that showed up at the Colosseum to watch the Christians burn.*

Nonetheless Romoff and Detre survived. "There's no way to have lasted for thirty-some years without learning to navigate these issues," Romoff says carefully. "This was constantly an adversarial world."

O'Connor says that when he first met with the university's search committee, one of its members characterized the health center as "a loose juggernaut that simply used resources and doesn't repay the campus." O'Connor soon learned differently. He and Dr. Detre, he recalls, "began to get together on a regular basis so I could learn the lay of the land. I found Detre actually quite gracious."

At the time, O'Connor and the university lacked a chief financial officer; Executive Vice President Jack E. Freeman had left in 1990. Detre offered to help.

THOMAS DETRE: *I said to Dennis, "If you think that you want it, then I'll come over with my team, and we will assist you for a period of time until you can create order, and then the university will be stronger," which is what we did. I was in his office three, four times a week. We discussed every aspect of the academic program, the financial issues underlying them. We sat afternoon after afternoon reviewing every damned thing, and that's how we became befriended.*

UPMC, under the leadership of Jeffrey A. Romoff and John Paul, assisted the chancellor until the arrival of a senior vice chancellor for business and finance in June 1992. There were those, of course, who decried Romoff's "influence" on O'Connor, but he and Thomas Detre remained on the chancellor's executive staff. "And from there on," says Detre, "I think Jeff and I became his favorite people because he realized that the evil empire meant work and reasonable order." O'Connor said in 2006, "I never asked [them] for anything that wasn't there in spades."

J. Dennis O'Connor, PhD (right), served as University of Pittsburgh chancellor from 1991 to 1995.

Romoff Advancing

The "conversion" of Chancellor O'Connor would have a profound effect on the future of the university and of UPMC. In 1992 Dr. Detre, then sixty-eight, told the chancellor that he wanted to retire in 1993 from his positions as senior vice chancellor for the Health Sciences and as president of UPMC. He also recommended that these two jobs be divided. They should be "interrelated but independent." He urged O'Connor to promote Romoff from vice chancellor for the Health Sciences at the University of Pittsburgh and executive vice president of UPMC to senior vice chancellor for health administration (a new position) and president of UPMC. O'Connor was reluctant; he urged Detre to stay on at least for a couple of years.

"The University of Pittsburgh's emergence as one of the country's most important medical research centers did not occur by accident."

— Arthur S. Levine, MD

Then, suddenly, Dr. Detre had a heart attack and found himself in intensive care. He soon underwent serious heart surgery. "But," he remembers, "before they dragged me to the operating room, I said to Dennis O'Connor, 'I hope I will recover from this, but I think the time has come to appoint Jeff to this position.' And so this was a perfect way of managing the transition!"

With UPMC Chair George Taber's and the board's approval, Romoff assumed many of Detre's duties at the hospitals as well as administration and financial control of the School of Medicine – predictably setting off a firestorm inside the university. The president of the faculty senate demanded to know why no national search had been conducted. In a poll of health sciences faculty about Romoff's appointment, 84 percent of the 825 people who voted said they favored a formal search. Nevertheless, the appointment stood.

JEFFREY A. ROMOFF: *Nobody wants the challenge of having aggressive people around. They're hard to manage. They're hard to control. So at every stage, at every stage in the evolution of UPMC, there was always substantial resistance. It engendered pushback at best. It left wounds. And thereby the resistance mounted. And the circle of people who either distrusted or resented ... whatever Dr. Detre and I and our colleagues represented, constantly widened.*

If academicians resented the fact that Romoff held a powerful medical school position without a medical degree, "It didn't do them any good!" laughs Julius Youngner, the distinguished, still youthful sole surviving member of the research team that created the Salk polio vaccine. "If they did, they were wasting their time."

They were shortsighted, too, Youngner might have added. Romoff and the WPIC team now controlled the clinical revenue of WPIC, Falk Clinic, Presbyterian, Eye & Ear, and Montefiore hospitals. Their shrewdness at managing these hospitals (and the take-no-prisoners style that offended many in academia at the time) helped to fund the University of Pittsburgh's growth trajectory as one of America's leading biomedical research institutions. At long last, the university-affiliated hospitals channeled substantial support to the university's medical education and research mission.

George K. Michalopoulos, MD, PhD

Romoff related well to researchers and found creative ways to fund their projects, according to George K. Michalopoulos, MD, PhD, chair of Pathology. Recruited to Pittsburgh from Duke University in 1991, Michalopoulos collaborated with Thomas Starzl, developed a pioneering molecular diagnostics division, and served as associate vice chancellor for the Health Sciences and interim dean of the School of Medicine from 1995 until 1998.

GEORGE MICHALOPOULOS: *Anything that could be defined as the desirable academic agenda, Jeff would be the one to implement it. That's the unique thing, because many places have great ideas. But where you find the resources to build the ideas is the most difficult thing; and that combination of the two, Jeff and Tom, allowed that to happen.*

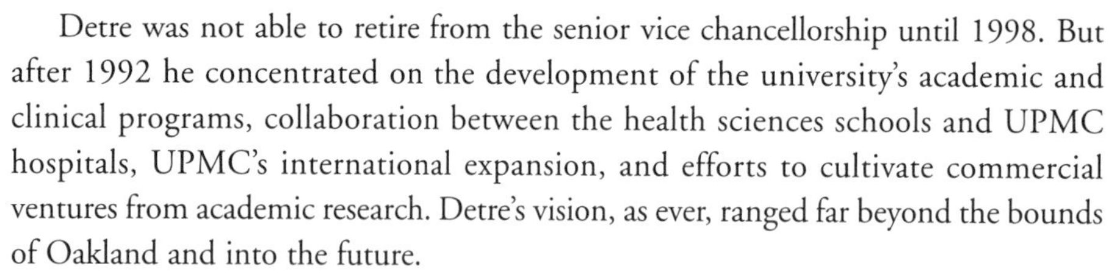

Detre was not able to retire from the senior vice chancellorship until 1998. But after 1992 he concentrated on the development of the university's academic and clinical programs, collaboration between the health sciences schools and UPMC hospitals, UPMC's international expansion, and efforts to cultivate commercial ventures from academic research. Detre's vision, as ever, ranged far beyond the bounds of Oakland and into the future.

"Over the past decade," he told a delegation from China in 1994, "our regional economy has shifted from one extremely dependent on heavy industry to a more diversified economy with clusters of technology-based, entrepreneurial companies. The local biomedical industry ... is forming an integral part of this emerging new economy."

Dr. Thomas Detre at home

PEACE

"Putting pieces together is a high-risk proposition. The natural state of humanity and of organizations is not to put pieces together. Keeping, insulating, protecting, navigating in the world you either created or lived in forever is the safe and comfortable place to be."

— Jeffrey A. Romoff

Creating a regional health care delivery system

1973 Congress passes the HMO Act of 1973, authorizing the federal government to help develop health maintenance organizations.

1994 National health expenditures reach 13.7 percent of Gross Domestic Product (GDP).

The failure of President Clinton's proposed plan for health care reform accelerates the rise of managed care as pressure to drive down rising costs intensifies.

In western Pennsylvania, the leading organizers of hospital networks are UPMC and the Allegheny Health, Education and Research Foundation (AHERF).

1996 Jeffrey A. Romoff tells the *Pittsburgh Post-Gazette*: "We are witnessing 'the conversion of health care from a social good to a commodity.'"

Managed care enrollment in western Pennsylvania grows from 350,000 in 1993 to 1.3 million in 1996.

1997 The federal Balanced Budget Act further reduces Medicare and Medicaid reimbursements.

UPMC is the top-ranking employer in the region, with 23,000 employees, up from 11,900 just a year earlier.

1998 AHERF declares the largest nonprofit medical bankruptcy in history.

1999 For the first time, UPMC achieves Honor Roll status in the annual ranking of the nation's best hospitals as compiled by *U.S. News & World Report.*

2000 Health care expenditures in the U.S. reach $1.7 trillion.

Liver transplant recipient
Yuleidi Mendoza, age five

6

Beyond Oakland

"Jeffrey Romoff wanted to change things; he wanted to put things on a business basis. He took advantage of managed care. Because if you didn't change, you were going to die." — Richard L. Simmons, MD

"We are undergoing a dramatic transformation in health care driven by market forces," Jeffrey A. Romoff announced to a roomful of stony-faced university physicians in 1995. "The economics of health care are changing as much as our science." UPMC, having created a strong academic medical center, had no time to rest on its laurels amid an "economic restructuring" of the U.S. health care system in the 1990s. The federal government and private insurers, fighting to curb galloping health care costs, tightened the reins on reimbursement. Health care became more commercial and profit-oriented as insurers tried to drive business to the provider who could offer "the lowest level of expense for services rendered."

High-cost academic medical centers were particularly vulnerable. And while neither Thomas Detre nor Jeffrey A. Romoff endorsed the commodification of health care, they fiercely defended the organization they and their colleagues had built. Lack of support for academic medical centers, Dr. Detre warned, "will condemn our citizens to a health care environment in which excellence is no longer an option."

The Anti-UPMC

Also a "huge, looming threat" to the fledgling UPMC was Allegheny General Hospital (AGH). Led by a mesmerizing president and a prominent board, AGH in the 1980s had hoped to strengthen its own position through some affiliation with the University of Pittsburgh. Detre had rebuffed that notion. His first allegiance, he said, was to the hospitals and physicians already associated with the university. "I told [AGH] that … the only time I could possibly include them as a component of an academic program was if my colleagues in the health center hospitals would deny my request to assist me," he recalled in 2005. He believes his response "infuriated" the AGH leaders.

So AGH crossed the state to Philadelphia, acquired four hospitals and two medical schools, and formed one of the largest health care systems in the country. Allegheny Health, Education and Research Foundation (AHERF), structured in July 1992, bought land in Pittsburgh's fast-growing northern suburbs, with the idea of competing with the university's School of Medicine. Passavant Hospital, in the nearby North Hills of Pittsburgh, looked on in dismay.

"Allegheny General was the anti-UPMC," contends Romoff.

"Everybody saw us as the white elephant in Oakland that was soon slated to disappear," believes George Michalopoulos.

"The CEO of the [Allegheny General] hospital declared to everybody that he was going to bury me alive," Detre remembers dryly.

At the Revolution

Like UPMC, AGH saw early on that independent, stand-alone hospitals had little chance of surviving in the managed care "revolution" that came swiftly to western Pennsylvania in the early 1990s. "Managed care products are network-based products," explains Dean Eckenrode, a former senior vice president of Blue Cross of Western Pennsylvania who would become a key executive in UPMC's insurance business. "They all purport to drive business to the most efficient provider, or at least the provider that is willing to provide services for the lowest reimbursement. And that was the new dynamic in western Pennsylvania."

Loren Roth, MD, MPH, a former student of Dr. Detre at Yale, has served UPMC and the University of Pittsburgh in a variety of significant roles.

Insurers pressed for price discounts and insisted on fewer hospitalizations and shorter lengths of stay. Hospitals and their employees had to find new ways to do more, faster, as did physicians. Managed care plans also put primary care physicians in the role of gatekeepers to both hospitals and medical specialists. These doctors would be paid a set fee per patient and be rewarded for limiting hospitalization and expensive diagnostic tests. Those who could not provide services efficiently enough would probably not survive. "The basic premise is that the best and most needed [hospitals] will prevail," Detre and Romoff had predicted in a 1988 position paper about national health care policy.

With the failure of President Clinton's health care reform plan in 1994, "the reaction was, the market will take over," remembers Loren Roth, then chief of Clinical Services at WPIC. "The insurance people assumed they were going to regulate us, and bring about this vision of decreased costs."

What came about instead was like the chaos that follows a poorly planned invasion. "We had great concern that we would be seeing fewer and fewer patients," George Huber recollects, "patients the academic medical center also needs for teaching and research."

"People were very frightened in 1993 to 1995," says Roth, who with his quicksilver mind created the job of UPMC's vice president for managed care in 1993. With revenues at risk, "We had to gather power," he adds. "Against whom? Against what we thought was the insurer. It was critically important that we, the university, needed to have friends."

Land rush fever seemed to sweep through western Pennsylvania health care. Patients became "customers." Everything seemed up for grabs: hospitals, physicians' practices, insurance contracts. Insurers as well as hospitals went on shopping sprees for primary care physician practices, because physicians controlled referrals to hospitals. Rumors flew about who was purchasing which physicians and facilities, or buying land, or opening primary care sites in neighborhood storefronts.

UPMC Vice Chair Mark J. Laskow, a lawyer and CEO of a financial advisory services firm, served at that time as a trustee of Shadyside Hospital. Shadyside was a financially healthy, nearly five-hundred-bed, advanced care institution located about two miles from the academic medical center. Its history dated back to 1866. But, Laskow remembers, "Consultants told us that the only way to survive in the future was to buy up your doctors and assure your admissions."

MARK LASKOW: *The problem was, we were essentially going to spend all of our cash buying physician practices – at prices where, with a tailwind on a very sunny day, we might break even on our purchase. Maybe. And then, at the end of that process, the strategy would either work, and we would be in business, kind of, or it would not work, and we would be out of money and ideas at the same time. Now I'm saying this in the context of a very healthy hospital. But everybody was looking down the road a number of years, and trying to understand how all of this was going to work.*

UPMC board officer Mark J. Laskow has compared UPMC hospital integration to the transformative industrialism of Pittsburgh's nineteenth century.

For Romoff, competition was energizing – including competition with Blue Cross of Western Pennsylvania, which would in 1996 merge with Pennsylvania Blue Shield to form Highmark, one of the largest health insurers in the nation.

JEFFREY A. ROMOFF: *UPMC has never come up against an adversary that wasn't, on the face of it, ten times stronger, whether it was the university to begin with, or Highmark. Of course, for me, that's the joy. Yes. Then it's a big-time play. The Goliaths usually control a lot of things that are really important. So taking on a Goliath is a real opportunity for UPMC.*

Making Friends Beyond the Ivory Tower

"*The health care community had often worried that if the university health center ever got its act together – if the sleeping giant ever awakened – it could be a formidable force.*"

— George A. Huber

UPMC resolved to reach "beyond the walls of the ivory tower" to build the strongest integrated health care system in the region. "We decided that the only way to control our destiny was to be at the top of the food chain," Scott Lammie puts it.

UPMC had to develop an efficient network "that wouldn't be bullied by Highmark," asserts David M. Farner, senior vice president, UPMC, and chief of staff, Office of the President.

"As separate entities, hospitals were vulnerable to divide-and-conquer tactics," says Sandra N. Danoff, who is senior vice president, UPMC, and chief communications officer. "The way to make things work was to have an integrated and cohesive network where you can provide highly specialized care to people close to home."

To better compete, UPMC pared costs at the Oakland hospitals and opened primary care centers in neighborhoods. In managed care terms, these were "access points" for "customers." At the same time, UPMC managers fanned out to area hospital administrators, medical staffs, and trustees "to convince all of these people that the best thing that could happen to them was to become part of UPMC," says C. Talbot Heppenstall Jr., senior vice president, UPMC, and treasurer.

George Huber remembers that "John Paul told me to go out and talk to every hospital I could possibly talk to, and convince them to be part of us." UPMC took the lead in stitching together Tri-State Health System, a network of community hospitals and their medical staffs. AGH did the same with its own network.

Leveraging and Counter-Leveraging

These were rambunctious years. Although UPMC was positioning itself for managed care under Blue Cross of Western Pennsylvania, it also supported the big insurer in its controversial 1994–1995 pitch to become the sole health insurance provider for the University of Pittsburgh, then the region's largest employer. UPMC backed Blue Cross over for-profit HealthAmerica because Blue Cross was willing, in this proposal, to subsidize the cost of academic medicine and medical education.

DEAN ECKENRODE: *In the [Blue Cross] proposal at that time was a benefit design that was based, at least partially, on the notion that if you delivered care in the right setting at the right time and with the right outcome, even if it was delivered in an expensive environment such as an academic medical center, in the long run it was as cheap or cheaper, from an insurance premium perspective, as care delivered in a less quality-efficient hospital. So part of that proposal was, let's call it, for lack of a better term, a research exercise, developing around that notion that the university hospitals, because they did things correctly and the outcomes were better, were in fact as cost effective as any other setting in which care might be delivered.*

The university's faculty and staff, however, were outraged to learn in March 1995 that they would no longer have a choice of health insurers for their personal medical coverage. Despite Romoff's argument that "when the university uses its fringe benefit pool to pay … for services that exclude university facilities, it is directly harming itself – the university," Dennis O'Connor's acceptance of the three-year, $66 million Blue Cross contract provoked catcalls and hissing in the university senate. The action proved to be O'Connor's last major decision as chancellor. He resigned just a few days later. Detractors of UPMC blamed O'Connor's troubles on the influence of Jeffrey A. Romoff.

Romoff was ferocious in protecting the academic medical center Detre and he had spent more than two decades building. "Jeffrey Romoff … made it clear this week that he is determined to see his institution come out a winner in whatever climate it must operate," the *Pittsburgh Post-Gazette* editorialized. As Romoff bluntly told physicians late in 1995, "In a competitive, commodity market, in order to survive you must amass the resources you need to compete favorably in that market." Some people found the rhetoric offensive, but "I had a high tolerance for not being liked," he would later say. "And we had developed a skill: We knew how to put pieces together."

Now UPMC bore down on the hospitals in its Tri-State network and others to consolidate into an integrated clinical enterprise with common governance, vision, mission, and financial incentives. In the spring and summer of 1996, nervous, skeptical CEOs and leaders from Tri-State hospitals held a series of strategy meetings to hammer out how they could "throw keys on the table" to form "a single economic unit." Everyone felt compelled to act fast. "The window of opportunity is closing quickly," read the meeting notes.

Rumors fed the sense of urgency: AGH was bleeding from its Philadelphia operations … for-profit Columbia/HCA had offered to buy Shadyside Hospital, and reportedly included with the sizeable cash offer was money to acquire more hospitals in the Pittsburgh area … St. Francis, Mercy, and West Penn hospitals in Pittsburgh were "heavily rumored" to be merging.

Tri-State Chair and UPMC Executive Vice President John Paul drove resolutely for integration, promising the hospitals they would survive only if they integrated. "John put a lot of pressure on a lot of people, but he was hell-bent on building a network," George Huber stresses. "He made a promise that if you integrated with us, you would realize a back-office savings alone of 20 to 30 percent of your existing costs."

St. Margaret Memorial Hospital opened in Pittsburgh's Lawrenceville neighborhood in 1910 and built a new hospital in Aspinwall in 1980 (right).

St. Margaret Memorial Hospital

Ultimately, UPMC had to convince the community hospitals' governing boards that an integrated health system would be right for western Pennsylvania. Although trustees had to make these decisions from a business perspective, distress and heartache often accompanied hospital affiliations, acquisitions, and mergers. Western Pennsylvania hospitals were longstanding community institutions, each with its own proud heritage and culture. As George L. W. Werner, dean emeritus of Trinity Episcopal Cathedral in downtown Pittsburgh, says longingly, "I loved St. Margaret."

GEORGE WERNER: *There was a feeling in that hospital that was so special, and so different. When our administrator, Stanley J. Kevish, walked down the hall, he not only said hello to every nurse and employee by name, but also asked about grandchildren by names. He had a staff that was phenomenal. And of all the boards I sat on, that was the one that was most transparent. The five of us on the executive committee would get phone calls on everything that was happening. It was a remarkable place doing a remarkable business, and I understood that that was going to change dramatically when we became one part of a much larger institution.*

George L. W. Werner, former trustee of St. Margaret Memorial Hospital and current director of UPMC and UPMC St. Margaret

On the morning when we made the decision to go with UPMC, I walked out to my car, and I sat there for a while, and I had one of my conversations with God. I sat there talking to God and saying, "Why?" I must have sat in that parking lot for half an hour. It was a very hard decision to make.

"But really I think we all tried to focus on what was good for the community," says Neil Van Horn, then the very hands-on chair of the St. Margaret Memorial Hospital board. "We were committed to building a

UPMC St. Margaret

A legacy from Pittsburgh iron and steel manufacturer John H. Shoenberger, St. Margaret Memorial Hospital was dedicated to his wife Margaret. It was later renamed UPMC St. Margaret.

Neil Van Horn chaired the St. Margaret Memorial Hospital board.

strong, community-focused, and community-owned health care delivery system. We wanted to be part of the winning network, and we could kind of see what UPMC might evolve into."

G. Nicholas Beckwith III, a prominent Pittsburgh business owner, investor, and civic leader, chaired the board of Shadyside Hospital. Like many Shadyside trustees, he could trace a strong family connection to the hospital. His father had chaired the board in the 1970s; Nick Beckwith had become a trustee in 1975.

G. NICHOLAS BECKWITH: *Shadyside in the early 1990s quickly saw a changed, increasingly competitive landscape. Despite a very loyal and large patient population, there was no assurance that our market niche or market share could remain the same; and it almost became one of those situations in which you are forced to say, "Do I try to tough it out doing what I have done successfully for a lot of years, or do I take what is seemingly and objectively a wiser course for the future based upon community dynamics as they then existed – but nonetheless a flip of a coin – and participate in some sort of merged entity?"*

Under the chandeliers of hospital boardrooms throughout western Pennsylvania, administrators, medical staffs, and trustees debated. Physicians everywhere feared a loss of autonomy, and community-based physicians in private practice felt threatened by the potential competition with academic physicians employed by the university. Administrators feared UPMC's reputation for top-down control. Employees worried about losing their jobs. Trustees were concerned about weakened community stewardship. Trustees and physicians warned Shadyside Hospital's chair that the UPMC merger would be "an earth-shattering failure." But UPMC's leaders believed that their "rational construct – academic excellence, clinical excellence, and community responsiveness" – was the right one.

Stained glass windows from the original hospital were moved to the new chapel in Aspinwall.

The first community hospital literally to give itself to UPMC was St. Margaret. The legacy of a nineteenth-century Episcopal industrialist as a memorial to his wife, the hospital in the early 1990s confronted managed care from a position of relative strength. The hospital had the advantages of one of the largest family practice residencies in the country, a good relationship with the University of Pittsburgh School of Medicine, and an involved and influential board of trustees. A leading member of the executive committee was the well-liked and quietly powerful Andrew W. Mathieson, vice president of Richard K. Mellon & Sons and a trustee and the treasurer of the Richard King Mellon Foundation. Along with George Taber,

Drew Mathieson had closely followed Detre's and Romoff's careers at the university. He trusted and endorsed their ambitions for the medical center, and he helped convince the St. Margaret board to take the bold step of turning control over to UPMC.

"The way George Taber or Drew Mathieson or later Nick Beckwith dealt with Detre and me," Romoff theorizes, "was to assess us, to understand our values, and then to embrace us and have us carry the ball. With St. Margaret, we jumped through a thousand hoops. I don't know how many retreats I had to present at. There were tons of delicate issues having to do with the well-being of people."

Drew Mathieson, George Werner, Neil Van Horn, and other trustees stipulated that St. Margaret's long tradition of community service would continue after their hospital's merger with UPMC. They also intended the merger to provide an impetus for others. "We wanted this network to be as strong as possible," said Mathieson, who died in 2001, "so we all spent time trying to convince our peers to join, too. The confident and amicable style with which we merged encouraged others. They saw that we achieved our goals. That made them more confident."

JEFFREY A. ROMOFF: *St. Margaret was the confirming merger. Presby was the merger that brought the academic medical center to UPMC, but it was the St. Margaret merger that legitimized us in the community.*

"Dr. Detre and Jeff Romoff saw that the hospital itself is just one element in a much larger, fully integrated system. What's important are the medical programs that already exist; then you integrate them and make them stronger."

— George A. Huber

Shadyside Hospital

Equally a turning point for UPMC was Shadyside Hospital. This large, well-managed hospital was, in Romoff's words, "the white-shoe hospital in town, at the top of its game." Shadyside's president was Henry Mordoh. Its board included many prominent Pittsburghers; some trustees were the second, third, or even fourth generation in their families to serve the hospital. Most of the Shadyside medical staff were private practitioners, and they had no desire to surrender autonomy to the university physicians. "A lot of our doctors had come from Montefiore, after the disruption there following the UPMC acquisition," notes Mark Laskow. "They all said, well, whatever you do, anybody but UPMC."

"That animosity I don't think could be overstated whatsoever," agreed the late UPMC director Donald D. Wolff Jr., then a Shadyside trustee. "And overcoming it was incredibly difficult."

G. NICHOLAS BECKWITH: *We had extensive debate between the board leadership and physician leaders, and it was very vocal and heated at times. And, I think, by and large, and understandably, the physicians wanted to do nothing other than continue*

SHADYSIDE HOSPITAL

Adding the South Wing in the 1950s

Shadyside Hospital opened in 1866 as the Homeopathic Medical and Surgical Hospital and Dispensary of Pittsburgh. The hospital moved from downtown Pittsburgh to the city's East End in 1910, and by the 1990s was large, well managed, and strong – but not prepared to stand alone against the managed care "revolution."

The hospital in the twenty-first century

Shadyside as it had been. The board was very much mixed, but I think, to a person, board leadership saw little choice.

As we were going through this multiple-year discussion, [we visited various organizations with which we might ally ourselves]. We did speak at some length, interestingly, with AHERF. And it was pretty quickly apparent that Shadyside might not be the best fit.

G. Nicholas Beckwith III chaired the board of Shadyside Hospital during negotiations with UPMC.

MARK LASKOW: *I think that there was a particular unhappiness there with their role in bidding for physicians' practices. There were very definite legal constraints on what you could pay for a practice. And we [at Shadyside] had been at pains to stay within those while still trying to be competitive. We would stretch to what we thought was the far side of the envelope, but within what the regulations and the laws allowed, in terms of buying practices – and then AGH would double it!*

That ... led you to question what the business practices were behind that. Because we just couldn't see any possible way they could achieve any positive cash flow or even neutral cash flow out of those prices. And we turned out to be right about that.

G. NICHOLAS BECKWITH: *We talked with the Cleveland Clinic. And we talked with [for-profit] Columbia/HCA at length, and some of our doctors were most enthused with that because they'd get some stock out of the deal. And lastly we talked independently with West Penn, but we were too similar to really create something new out of that relationship. That would have been a study in repetition.*

But the last such conversation I started then as chairman was, through George Taber, with Jeff Romoff. UPMC was growing more demonstrative and better known – I wouldn't want to use the term "a rattler of sabers," but it was increasingly a feared entity. And Jeff, whom I had not met at that point in time, was one of those personas within this community that was a little bit larger than life, and with that comes a little bit of natural fear on the part of any counterpart. So at the very least we understood we had to get to know this guy and try and understand where he would play in the future either as an enemy or as part of some united agency. We had a series of phone sessions thereafter, talking about philosophy. On occasion in raised tones of voice, maybe mine more so than his. But that ultimately led, after a lot of drafts of a merger agreement, to our merger, on, of all days, April Fool's Day of 1997.

JEFFREY A. ROMOFF: *Nick understood the direction of UPMC, and he understood that I was driven as its leader. He understood [our] track record. So if he was going to make a coin toss, the real calculation he had to make is, "Can I trust this guy? Do I believe he's actually going to get where he wants to be?"*

The great thing that differentiated Shadyside was that they knew what they wanted. Nick wanted Shadyside to be a center of excellence, and Shadyside could have this if he joined with us. And to know that is really a brilliant thing. It requires a sense of vision that not a lot of people have.

The negotiation with Shadyside was a gentleman's negotiation. It was excruciating; it took too long, and it was too detailed, and all of that, but when negotiations ended, and we took over Shadyside, Nick 100 percent bought into it. He did the merger to bring academic excellence to Shadyside, to make it sterling and superb. That was the purpose of the merger: to rebirth Shadyside to be great.

Shadyside intended to keep its resources at play in the acute care hospital business, "as opposed to taking our liquid net worth out of the business and putting it into a foundation which might have been only tangentially associated," Beckwith says. "It struck me that the proper thing to do, since we were going to work on this together, was to devote everything to the primary mission."

JEFFREY A. ROMOFF: *So St. Margaret and Shadyside, one right after another, really carried the regional wave. They were legitimizing acts. That made us very hard to beat by any stretch of the imagination, as long as we produced.*

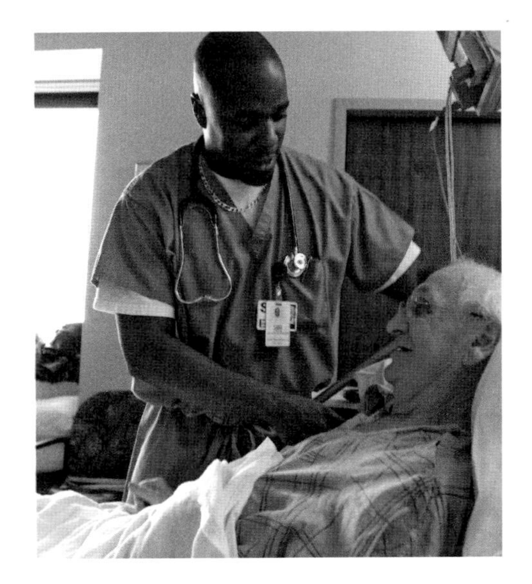

Shadyside Hospital opened the first school of nursing in Pittsburgh in 1884 and still operates one of the region's largest hospital-based schools of nursing.

LOREN ROTH: *To my way of thinking, the merger with Shadyside was the most important thing we did in the creation of UPMC. This is my view. Unadulterated. There would be no UPMC today without the Shadyside merger.*

JEFFREY A. ROMOFF: *The merger of Shadyside was not about UPMC's "having" Shadyside. It was putting the pieces together; it was adding to the pieces to create a greater whole.*

Hillman Cancer Center

Beckwith and the Shadyside board, intent on keeping their hospital in service to the community, had negotiated for UPMC's shifting a center of excellence from the Oakland campus to UPMC Shadyside. This would become Hillman Cancer Center, the hub of the University of Pittsburgh Cancer Institute (UPCI).

Hillman Cancer Center was made possible through a lead gift of $10 million from the Henry L. Hillman Foundation, the Hillman Foundation, and Henry L. Hillman. The donation represented the largest single gift in UPMC's history up to that time. The Shadyside Hospital Foundation raised a record $45 million for the project.

Henry Hillman, Elsie Hillman, and Ronald B. Herberman, MD (left to right)

Hillman Cancer Center opened on the UPMC Shadyside campus in 2002, bringing together for the first time under one roof UPCI's clinical and research components. Ensuring world-class cancer care for the people of western Pennsylvania and far beyond, it also secured a strong future for Shadyside, the hospital Henry and Elsie Hilliard Hillman's families had served and governed for generations.

By the twenty-first century, Hillman Cancer Center would become the nucleus for UPMC Cancer Centers, one of the largest integrated community networks of cancer physicians and specialists in the country. The latest advances in cancer prevention, detection, diagnosis, and treatment would flow from there to locations surrounding Pittsburgh and in adjacent states, as well as internationally. No longer would patients have to leave their communities to receive the highest level of cancer care.

Hillman Cancer Center

A condition of Shadyside Hospital's joining UPMC was that a center of excellence would become part of the hospital campus. This promise was fulfilled with the 2002 opening of Hillman Cancer Center, made possible through a lead gift from the Henry L. Hillman Foundation, the Hillman Foundation, and Henry L. Hillman. The sculpture "Spirits' Flight" highlights the connection between art and healing.

Hurdles to Integration

In just a few years UPMC had swelled to seventeen hospitals, twenty-five thousand employees, a post-acute care network, and more than three hundred "access points." Its market share in western Pennsylvania was 20 percent; more than 90 percent of western Pennsylvania's residents lived within thirty minutes of a UPMC hospital. UPMC had become the area's largest employer.

In 1998, however, most people in the Pittsburgh region had almost no idea what UPMC was, or meant, or stood for. A similar confusion permeated the suddenly huge organization. "Mergers always look good on paper," observes George Werner, who became a UPMC director. "They look like they will work, and they look like they make sense, but once you start mixing cultures, as the corporate world knows, it's a lot different."

"The integration periods were the real hard parts," agrees Tal Heppenstall, who was UPMC's investment banker before becoming treasurer in 2003.

"We were literally feeling our way," admits Neil Van Horn, who became a UPMC director when St. Margaret Memorial Hospital joined UPMC.

"And we held cost-per-case constant during this entire period. That's completely unheard of."

— Sandra N. Danoff

Significant barriers to integration threatened the fragile new structure. Physicians and employees outside the university distrusted "Oakland" and its power. The hospitals still thought in their own silos, parochial thinking that led to competition among members who needed to cooperate. Leadership structures, performance evaluation, and performance incentives remained fixed on old organization paradigms. Greater efficiencies had to be introduced and lengths-of-stay at all hospitals had to be reduced. Physicians resisted the elimination or relocation of virtually any clinical support service. Community hospital administrators and boards were reluctant to lay off employees or pull business from local vendors, jeopardizing the system's efficiencies and productivity. All the individual HR policies and information and billing systems that people had grown comfortable with had to change. Capital was needed for investment in infrastructure and information technology. The board was concerned about whether UPMC had the "depth of management talent" to handle the rapid growth, according to UPMC director Martin G. McGuinn, retired chairman and CEO of Mellon Financial Corporation.

The challenge was to centralize this unwieldy new entity, to make it efficient and profitable, and to do it fast, because Jeffrey A. Romoff never let up.

C. Talbot Heppenstall Jr., senior vice president, UPMC and treasurer

Senior vice president, UPMC and chief of staff, Office of the President, David M. Farner has played a key role as UPMC expanded in the past twenty years.

DAVID FARNER: *The years from 1997 to 2001 were, I call them, pure hell. Working, changing, consolidating. We were merging proud institutions where the CEO had been the CEO for ten or fifteen years. The CFO used to oversee payroll and IT; now that's all done over at University Center. Now what we need the CFO to be focused on is how do I improve and run the business. It was a different skill set, it was a different understanding of the business. It was a change times ten – all these different institutions we were asking to change.*

SANDRA DANOFF: *As difficult as it was – and it was both painful and difficult – we set about creating a network and pursuing efficiencies. It sounds simple, but it required sheer force of will from the entire leadership team. And frankly, it was not fun! But … it drove people to find more efficient ways of doing what they did. And we held cost-per-case constant during this entire period. That's completely unheard of. So I think that's a measure of the success.*

ROBERT CINDRICH: *The benefits of revenue-cycle management, the benefits of the supply-chain management, and the ability to purchase in bulk – all these things devolve down to every part of UPMC. There are benefits; there's no way to get them on your own.*

"What UPMC's creators did uniquely well was to bring businesslike discipline to hospital operations," according to a UPMC overview published in the journal *Academic Medicine.* "By creating a truly integrated system, UPMC achieved savings in 'back office' functions approaching 30 percent."

Elizabeth B. Concordia, executive vice president, UPMC and president, Hospital and Community Provider Services Division, says that when she was recruited from Johns Hopkins in 2001, her first charge was to merge UPMC Presbyterian and UPMC Shadyside. "There was certainly a lot of internal pressure to get the hospitals to start turning an operating profit," she remembers. "We went into a very focused operational review and cost consciousness of how we were running the institutions." And, she adds, "When you look at wanting to make changes, you need to make that change tomorrow, not three years from now. Analyze, act, and don't be afraid to make mistakes."

C. TALBOT HEPPENSTALL: *If you look around the country, at other systems, they never got past signing the original affiliation agreement. They say they're a health system, but they're really independent hospitals that borrow money together. But UPMC is essentially run by one management team. And that's what makes it completely different – but that was a huge risk. Because when UPMC was signing all these affiliation agreements, everybody thought … you're never going to be able to pull this integration off.*

Dead wrong.

THE EVOLUTION OF UPMC'S WESTERN PENNSYLVANIA HOSPITALS

1949

Management of Western Psychiatric Institute and Clinic (WPIC), previously state-run, transferred to University of Pittsburgh

WESTERN PSYCHIATRIC INSTITUTE AND CLINIC (WPIC)

1965

University Health Center of Pittsburgh (UHCP) incorporated

UPMC MONTEFIORE

1973

Thomas Detre, MD, joins the University of Pittsburgh as chair of Psychiatry

1985

Management of Eye & Ear Hospital assumed by University of Pittsburgh

UPMC PRESBYTERIAN

1986

University of Pittsburgh forms Medical and Health Care Division (MHCD)

MHCD manages WPIC, Eye & Ear Hospital, and Presbyterian-University Hospital

1990

MHCD changes name to University of Pittsburgh Medical Center (UPMC)

Presbyterian-University Hospital acquires Montefiore Hospital

UPMC BEDFORD MEMORIAL

1992

WPIC merged into UPMC Presbyterian

1993

UPMC Montefiore merged into UPMC Presbyterian

1996

The South Side Hospital of Pittsburgh, Aliquippa Hospital Association, and Braddock Medical Center join UPMC

UPMC BRADDOCK

1997

St. Margaret Memorial, Shadyside, and North Hills Passavant Hospitals join UPMC

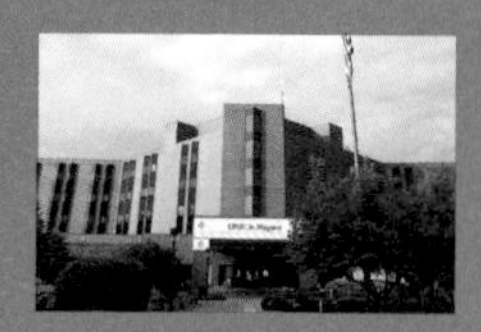

UPMC ST. MARGARET

UPMC SHADYSIDE

UPMC McKEESPORT

UPMC PASSAVANT – McCANDLESS CAMPUS

UPMC PASSAVANT – CRANBERRY CAMPUS

CHILDREN'S HOSPITAL OF PITTSBURGH OF UPMC

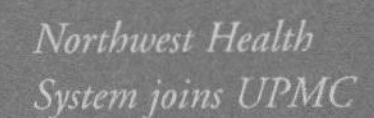

1998

The Rehabilitation Institute of Pittsburgh, McKeesport Hospital, Lee Hospital, Memorial Hospital of Bedford County, and Horizon Hospital System join UPMC

1999

Magee-Womens Hospital joins UPMC

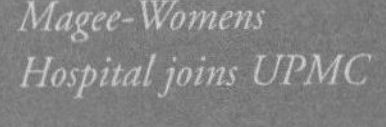

MAGEE-WOMENS HOSPITAL OF UPMC

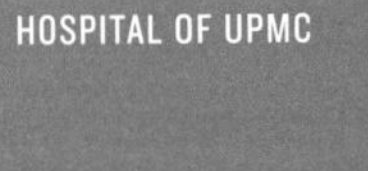

2001

Northwest Health System joins UPMC

UPMC Beaver Valley (formerly Aliquippa Hospital) returned to community control

Children's Hospital of Pittsburgh signs integration agreement with UPMC

2002

Hillman Cancer Center opens on the UPMC Shadyside campus

2003

UPMC Presbyterian and UPMC Shadyside merge

2004

New UPMC Northwest in Franklin formally dedicated

UPMC Passavant Cranberry opens

2005

UPMC Rehabilitation Hospital consolidated into UPMC South Side

UPMC Lee Regional sold to local health system

2007

UPMC Passavant Cranberry merges into UPMC Passavant

2008

The Mercy Hospital of Pittsburgh joins UPMC

Oil City campus of UPMC Northwest closes

2009

New Children's Hospital of Pittsburgh of UPMC formally dedicated

UPMC South Side merges into UPMC Mercy

UPMC HORIZON – GREENVILLE CAMPUS

UPMC HORIZON – SHENANGO CAMPUS

UPMC NORTHWEST

UPMC MERCY

An Agreement Is an Agreement

In putting together its network of community hospitals, UPMC in some cases saved a community hospital from closing; in others, it created a charitable foundation to support health care in the community. UPMC very rarely "bought" a hospital. And over time the system has been refined. In 2001, for example, UPMC transferred the ownership of UPMC Beaver Valley (formerly Aliquippa Hospital) back to a nonprofit community group, which operated the hospital until it closed in 2008. In 2005 the system sold UPMC Lee Regional in Johnstown to Conemaugh Health System.

But by 2001 UPMC had the strength to withstand a member hospital's attempt to, in Romoff's words, "be liberated from" its merger agreement, an attempt that ultimately strengthened UPMC in new ways. UPMC Passavant, contending that it had concerns about UPMC's strategic direction and finances, announced publicly in March 2000 that it wished to withdraw from the system. Passavant now was making money, and was no longer threatened by AGH moving into its territory. AHERF, having amassed $1.3 billion in debt, had declared the largest nonprofit medical system bankruptcy in history.

Passavant served a formal demand for binding arbitration of its disputes with UPMC. Romoff remembers it as also a personal attack on him and his leadership. Rather than retreat he immediately informed the board about the contents of what he terms a "blackmail document." In a complex and expensive JAMS arbitration (Judicial Arbitration and Mediation Services), UPMC vigorously defended its contract and its integrity. UPMC also interposed a substantial counter claim, citing "failures by UPMC Passavant to cooperate with contractually required integration of the hospital into the system," according to Edwin L. Klett, UPMC's attorney in the arbitration. In November 2001 the three-member arbitration panel affirmed the merger agreement and ordered that Passavant had to stay with UPMC.

Klett believes "everyone benefited to some extent from that exercise."

EDWIN KLETT: *I think it demonstrated to the member hospitals, as well as to the system, that an agreement is an agreement is an agreement. And that seller remorse, which was really at the heart of the Passavant problem, was not going to get you out of the system. Trying to embarrass the management of UPMC, alleging bad conduct and bad intentions, really backfired. And I think there's a larger impact too. I think the system benefited from hearing firsthand from a member hospital as to how onerous and perhaps dictatorial some of the [integration] practices were. I think the [system] now is much more user-friendly.*

"How do you go out and re-engineer the delivery system on a regional basis and get out of the cottage industry? If you don't get people to merge systems, merge programs, actually drive efficiencies and work collaboratively, you really haven't integrated. I think the beauty of the UPMC model is that there has to be a single governance and a single set of decisions made."

— Scott Lammie

Changing the Governance Paradigm

Judge Robert J. Cindrich chaired the board of South Side Hospital at the time of its acquisition by UPMC in 1996. He points out that "the ownership, if you will, of a nonprofit is comprised of whoever has the power to appoint and remove the board."

In its expanding system, UPMC relied on the shared governance model that had defined the relationship of Presbyterian-University Hospital with the University of Pittsburgh. There the governing board was comprised of about half UPMC-appointed community directors and half university-appointed directors. Now each hospital that joined UPMC gained representation and a governance role on the UPMC Board of Directors. The new board was one-third UPMC-appointed, one-third university-appointed, and one-third appointed from the community hospitals. "So part of creating the new system was we have to cede power in order to grow," David Farner points out.

The Passavant dispute came at a time when the UPMC governing board was growing not only in size but also in influence. Many new directors from the community hospitals were determined to be fully engaged in the life of the organization so they could provide true stewardship, especially in the wake of the AHERF bankruptcy, where trustees had found themselves publicly criticized and embarrassed for lack of awareness of critical issues.

UPMC Passavant's unsuccessful attempt in 2001 to secede from UPMC in fact strengthened the young health system in several ways.

In their negotiations with UPMC, the Shadyside Hospital trustees had insisted on maintaining a significant influence within the overall governance of UPMC.

G. NICHOLAS BECKWITH: *Shadyside's position was that if we were going to do this, we would have a prominent seat at the table. Not a dominating seat at the table, but one through which we could voice what we believed was proper for this then-young system.*

St. Margaret Memorial Hospital board members, too, "had been very active day-to-day players in our institution," Neil Van Horn recalls. "We made the commitment when we merged that we'd get involved, and that's what we did."

Along with stewardship, the new directors brought to the UPMC board their awareness of the financial complexity of the health care business.

MARK LASKOW: *All the board members have operated businesses, and they know that there are in fact problems in businesses. So they know there is a certain air of unreality if they sit in a board meeting and real problems aren't discussed as such. Not just opportunities or challenges, but problems. It's much more relaxed for everyone and I think easier on management if everybody can sit there and say, "Well, you know, this is actually a tough business, and things are going to go wrong sometimes, but here's how we're going to attack these things."*

Shadyside Hospital, for instance, had done a lot of due diligence on the economics of UPMC's purchases of physician practices. So at one of the first UPMC board meetings Mark Laskow attended, when the budget was proposed, he asked, "Do these projected income figures include the losses on the purchased practices?"

"Yes," answered Romoff.

Suddenly a longtime UPMC board member sat up in his seat. "What losses?" he demanded. The losses were in fact accounting procedures that transferred certain revenues from the practices to the hospitals. But to Laskow, the question and the ensuing discussion were important steps toward transparency.

"So the board formed a committee to oversee the practices, and a lot of board time was spent on it," he recalls. "Nothing bad happened to management over this; the directors knew that this is what had been going on; we just started to deal with the consequences in an open way, and that was that. And that's why it turned out to be constructive for everybody. I think the existing UPMC board was ready for a little bit of a paradigm shift."

Beckwith, Laskow, and Donald Wolff pushed UPMC to establish a committee to oversee health care quality. "If you adopt the attitude that you're actually representing the community and the patient, it's the right thing to do, as opposed to representing specifically the economic interests of the system," said Wolff, who before his death in 2008 chaired the Quality Committee. The Donald D. Wolff Jr. Center for Quality Improvement and Innovation at UPMC was named in his honor.

The late Donald D. Wolff Jr. served as a trustee of Shadyside Hospital and director of UPMC.

Beckwith succeeded Richard L. Fischer as chair of the UPMC board in 2002. He defines the board's executive committee as "an exceedingly successful group of governors – as good as I've ever seen." Romoff describes Beckwith as "one of the finest community leaders I have had the opportunity to work with. He is a gentleman and a consumate leader and is absolutely committed to the success of UPMC. And that is essential. That is essential."

JEFFREY A. ROMOFF: *I think part of the recent success, the rapidity with which we are changing and growing, has a great deal to do with Nick. He definitely enhances UPMC.*

Challenging itself to create a new high-water mark in good governance and to achieve best-in-class standards for governance, transparency, and operational performance, UPMC in 2006 became America's first and only nonprofit health enterprise to fully adopt and receive auditor's certification for Sarbanes-Oxley implementation. This law was enacted in the wake of the Enron accounting scandals. UPMC's adoption of the new standards included the stringent requirements of Section 404, which calls for full, independent attestation about the organization's financial condition and internal control efficacy. UPMC would also adopt public financial disclosure practices for both quarterly and annual results, allowing community stakeholders to review its progress and fiscal health.

"Our board viewed Sarbanes-Oxley 404 certification as a best-in-class practice," comments Robert A. DeMichiei, senior vice president, UPMC and chief financial officer. "We wanted to set the bar higher for ourselves, or as high as you could for a for-profit company," says DeMichiei, who joined UPMC from GE Energy in 2004.

About UPMC's surprisingly rapid years of expansion and subsequent advances, Beckwith comments, "It has been fascinating for me, and a privilege for me, to see what was small and misunderstood and fumbling like a newborn child in 1997 grow into what it is today."

"God, if Drew Mathieson could see how this has evolved!" marvels Neil Van Horn about his late friend and fellow St. Margaret trustee. "Drew had these big ideas and this vision, but if he could see what's happened, he would absolutely be blown away."

"Much of UPMC's development was guided by our vision of what we needed to do to evolve as an integrated system over time – just basically what we needed to do to survive to get to the next step."

— Scott Lammie

Orchestrating an integrated health care delivery and financing system

1995 In order to adapt to the changing health care environment and to continue to promote the organization's academic mission, a new corporate organizational structure under the University of Pittsburgh Medical Center System (UPMCS) is approved; it includes corporate entities to pursue activities in the areas of insurance and health delivery and related ventures.

1996 Blue Cross of Western Pennsylvania and Pennsylvania Blue Shield merge to form Highmark Inc., the largest health insurer in Pennsylvania.

UPMC enters the health insurance business as Best Health Care of Western Pennsylvania.

1997 UPMC's insurance company, Best Health Care, files for commercial HMO and PSO products and changes its name to UPMC Health Plan.

Simultaneously with the major expansion of UPMC's hospital operations, physician practices, and health insurance, UPMC begins providing health-related products and services that comprise a pre- and post-acute care service continuum.

1998 UPMC and the University of Pittsburgh reach a ten-year agreement wherein UPMC pledges $1 billion in support of the university's research and academic enterprise over the course of the agreement. The two organizations become separate entities, yet intertwined through board representation. UPMC administrators now report directly to the board of directors of the UPMCS.

The University of Pittsburgh's physician practice plans are integrated by UPMC into University of Pittsburgh Physicians (UPP).

Arthur S. Levine, MD, of the National Institutes of Health, becomes senior vice chancellor for the Health Sciences and dean of the School of Medicine.

1999 Magee-Womens Hospital becomes part of UPMC.

2001 Children's Hospital of Pittsburgh agrees to join UPMC.

2002 UPMC and Highmark agree to a new contract.

2008 The Mercy Hospital of Pittsburgh merges with UPMC.

1995–2008

Mercy Hospital

7

Reinventing UPMC

"So Jeff went from most hated to most admired because ... all the opposing CEOs and boards essentially [became] part of the same troops. And then they saw that this was really good – for the institutions, for the community, for the hospital, for people." — Richard L. Simmons, MD

"We had developed a skill: we knew how to put pieces together."

— Jeffrey A. Romoff

To survive in the turbulent health care market of the mid- to late-1990s, UPMC transformed itself into more than a regional hospital network. UPMC at the same time set off beyond the bounds of traditional revenue generation to "re-engineer the delivery system" and to expand, diversify, and consolidate – to "participate in every element of the managed care premium dollar." And even though clinical reimbursements continued to decline in this hectic time, UPMC's leaders kept faith in the eventual success of the integrated health delivery and financing system they were putting together. They kept faith too in the mission: the synergy of research, teaching, and outstanding patient care. UPMC's investment in the University of Pittsburgh "did not falter."

That faith was sorely tested in the '90s, when UPMC seemed to be running on vision and little more. Wrestling regional hospitals into a system (and losing millions on operations), UPMC also took bold financial steps to sustain its operations and capitalization and build its infrastructure.

"The risks kept getting bigger and bigger and bigger," says UPMC Senior Vice President and Treasurer Tal Heppenstall. The former investment banker's job was to convince the markets to lend to an organization whose future seemed unpredictable at best. "'Are they really going to take on Highmark?'" Heppenstall remembers the lenders asking. "'Are they going to have enough money to take on Highmark? How come they're not the next AHERF?' – which in the municipal bond market was the equivalent of Enron in the stock market."

"Much of UPMC's development was guided by our vision of what we needed to do to evolve as an integrated system over time," says Scott Lammie, a longtime member of UPMC's brain trust. "How and when we got there had much to do with the business environment, the people, and the partnering options presented to us. A lot of our success was just basically what do you need to do to survive to get to the next step."

Over the years Lammie has parlayed his forensic accounting skills and business acumen into analyzing, creating, or straightening out complex business operations within UPMC. He remembers the day "we were sitting in a room strategizing – how are we going to preserve our ability to invest in the academic mission? We decided that the only way that we could actually enhance the mission was to diversify."

In 1995 the organization's board approved a new corporate organizational structure enabling UPMC to pursue activities in the areas of insurance and other health ventures. Lammie became the executive vice president and chief financial officer of UPMC Diversified Services when it started up in January 1996.

"Our intent was to deliver comprehensive health care services across the region, creating scalable service delivery platforms that were cost-effective and structured to derive optimal economics and great clinical outcomes," he explains. What followed was "nearly a decade of putting pieces together."

Scott Lammie, vice president of Finance, Insurance Services Division, and chief financial officer, UPMC Health Plan

"What Are You Trying to Tell Us — You Know How to Do Insurance?"

By 1996 UPMC had a complicated relationship with the region's dominant health insurer, Blue Cross of Western Pennsylvania. UPMC competed with Blue Cross to buy physician practices and relentlessly put together a hospital network with enough clout to negotiate effectively with the insurer. On the other hand, UPMC partnered with Blue Cross in 1996, acquiring an interest in the insurer's start-up Security Blue Medicare HMO (which UPMC would sell back in 2000).

Then in late 1996 Blue Cross of Western Pennsylvania merged with Pennsylvania Blue Shield to form Highmark Inc., with a 60 to 65 percent market share in western Pennsylvania. UPMC worried that the big insurer would overwhelm and ultimately dominate the market. John Paul, UPMC's hard-driving executive vice president, had an idea.

George A. Huber, UPMC's first chief counsel

GEORGE HUBER: *"Look," John said, "maybe we ought to start thinking about somehow investing in or owning our own health maintenance organization." And at the same time, John said, "Maybe Highmark would be interested in having us partner with them. It would be a Highmark–UPMC-unique insurance company."*

Their response to that was, "What are you trying to tell us – you know how to do insurance? We'll tell you what we'll do. We'll let you be a little component of that partnership, but we want to dominate. We want to control." This is how we read it. Our response to that was, "Baloney. You know what we're going to do? We're going to start our own insurance business."

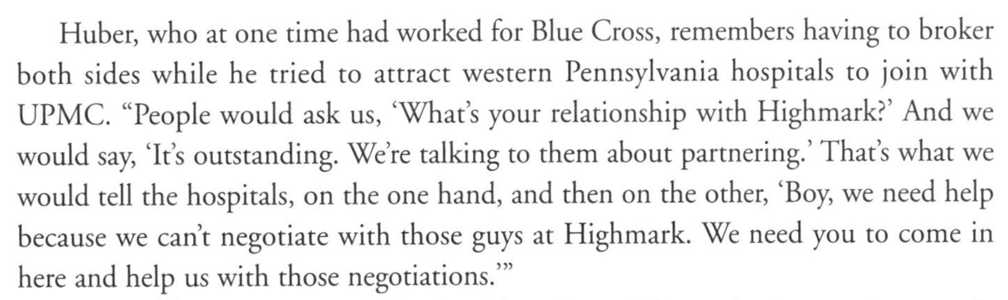

Huber, who at one time had worked for Blue Cross, remembers having to broker both sides while he tried to attract western Pennsylvania hospitals to join with UPMC. "People would ask us, 'What's your relationship with Highmark?' And we would say, 'It's outstanding. We're talking to them about partnering.' That's what we would tell the hospitals, on the one hand, and then on the other, 'Boy, we need help because we can't negotiate with those guys at Highmark. We need you to come in here and help us with those negotiations.'"

Former Blue Cross Senior Vice President Dean Eckenrode also reveals an angle that UPMC did not know at the time.

DEAN ECKENRODE: *Blue Cross had actually made a proposal in the eastern area of its range, out in Blair County, to absorb a major hospital and its owned physician practices. The deal did not come to fruition. So when UPMC made its decision to get an HMO license, the notion [from outside] was, they're jumping into the Blue Cross business. Well, Blue Cross was literally considering jumping into the hospital business as well.*

John Paul insisted that UPMC had to have its own Medicaid HMO "because of the state's likely shift to managed care Medicaid plans," he told a reporter in 1995. "Medicaid reimbursements are lower than those of private insurers, and having an HMO … will enable UPMC 'to cut out the middleman.'" In 1996 UPMC acquired a partnership interest in Best Health Care, a Medicaid HMO. Best Health Care would file for commercial HMO and POS products and change its name to UPMC Health Plan in 1997.

Dean Eckenrode

Paul convinced Eckenrode to join UPMC. The two then recruited a number of experienced insurance executives to shepherd UPMC's emerging insurance venture.

Diane P. Holder, who would become president of UPMC's Health Insurance Division, served at the time as president of Western Psychiatric Institute and Clinic (WPIC), one of the largest psychiatric hospitals in the country. However, she remembers, "the big, coming threat" was Pennsylvania's plan to be one of the first states in the country to enroll all Medicaid beneficiaries in managed care. "So Western Psych looked like a complete sitting duck."

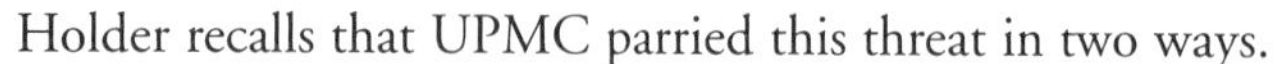

Holder recalls that UPMC parried this threat in two ways.

DIANE HOLDER: *First we had to find much less expensive ways to deliver care. We brought our cost level down to the point that we could actually take contracts from companies that typically would not pay you much more than a 5 or 10 percent premium over what they would pay a standard hospital, even though we were one of the very best in the country. So we fought to preserve the mission, which was to give people excellent clinical care, and we fought to preserve the research environment. Had either been hurt or damaged … it would have been a tragedy.*

The second strategy was an innovative venture, Community Care Behavioral Health, a nonprofit managed care organization. "It seemed to many of us that if you could actually become part of the financing vehicle, you would be in a much, much better position to continue to drive clinical excellence and to support the ability to continue the grant funding for research," Holder says.

But, she remembers, "When we started Community Care, we had no members. We had nothing, absolutely nothing. We had a piece of paper with a name on it. When I think back on it now, it's like those mountain climbers who tell you not to look at the top of the mountain. Just see the next cliff."

Other health providers had tried starting insurance companies in the 1990s.

SANDRA DANOFF: *At that time there was a move afoot for provider networks to "assume risk." While these provider networks agreed to provide coverage to a population of patients for a fixed cost, most didn't have the information systems to do it; they didn't have the physician network to do it; so they were in effect saying, "I'm going to get paid a fixed amount for something over which I have very little control of the cost."*

UPMC tried a different approach. Community Care cut its teeth by acting as a behavioral health vendor to UPMC's Best Health Care, the Medicaid HMO that also was taking its first steps.

SANDRA DANOFF: *Instead, we learned to do this within our walls on our own employees. It raises the stakes. You have to do it right because you have to sit across the table from the people it affects. We learned what was really required. What was the information that you needed to make good decisions? What were the things that people loved and hated? It was an ongoing process of analysis and adjustment. It wasn't simply an experiment in cost reduction.*

Mostly this success came from the people who had to deliver the care. They had figured out how to do things differently than they had in the past. How to do it better.

The big prize for Community Care was winning the five-year, $500 million contract to manage behavioral health services for Medicaid beneficiaries in Allegheny County, the second-most populous county in Pennsylvania. "We bid against all the big players, and we worked very, very hard to demonstrate to Allegheny County leadership and to the state that we were the best choice," says Holder.

DIANE HOLDER: *We brought to the table every senior clinical person from WPIC who could help us. "What's the best way you help people with schizophrenia?" "What's the best way you help children with attention deficit disorders?" "How do you really make sure you're doing these things well and right?" We analyzed statewide financial data, so that by the time we ultimately bid and negotiated, our final capitated dollar amount was within three cents of our original proposal.*

"We fought to preserve the mission, which was to give people excellent clinical care, and we fought to preserve the research environment. Had either been hurt or damaged … it would have been a tragedy."

— Diane P. Holder

Diane P. Holder, executive vice president, UPMC; president, Insurance Services Division; and president, UPMC Health Plan

That was the methodology from WPIC: You had to be very fiscally focused; you had to make sure you had the dollars you needed; you negotiated hard; and when you got the money, then you did the right thing with your money. I was very proud when Community Care received an ethics award from the American Association of Community Psychiatrists.

UPMC's investment to launch its insurance business was a bold move for an organization already pouring hundreds of millions of dollars into mergers and capital improvements. But for UPMC there were two decisive reasons to take that risk. First, UPMC managers wanted to counter what they saw as Highmark's intent to dominate the provider community. And UPMC believed it could develop a true health maintenance organization, one that would manage care as well as costs.

"What started out simply as a way to gain a foothold in the medical assistance, managed care business grew quickly into an opportunity to become an integrated health care delivery and financing system."

— DEAN ECKENRODE

DEAN ECKENRODE: *What started out simply as a way to gain a foothold in the medical assistance, managed care business grew quickly into an opportunity to become an integrated health care delivery and financing system. Under an integrated delivery system, all elements of the health care equation are supposed to work effectively together. So the same people are managing your premium and managing your illness and promoting your wellness; there is no contradictory incentive as one might see in a more traditional relationship where both the insurer and the provider have to find profit at the employer's or the enrollee's expense.*

The versatile Scott Lammie took on a new job: senior vice president, Insurance Services Division, and chief financial officer, UPMC Health Plan. "Today," he observes, "there's a huge paradigm shift that's beginning to emerge, with the realization that the best entity to deliver the required wellness services and capabilities is the insurance arm."

DIANE HOLDER: *If we're smart fiscal stewards, we have the opportunity to improve health care and health outcomes for people.*

Jeffrey A. Romoff, on the other hand, was not at first enthusiastic about UPMC going into the insurance business. He derided insurance as "ticket-scalping" rather than innovative care, research, or education. But he was ready to compete with Highmark. "Jeff saw insurance more, I think, as a strategic necessity," Eckenrode surmises.

Within ten years of UPMC's purchase of a single HMO license, UPMC Health Plan became one of the country's fastest-growing health insurance plans, offering an array of commercial, Medicare, and Medicaid products. While the Health Plan is small compared to Highmark, the National Committee for Quality Assurance recognized it as one of the top insurance plans in the nation and ranked it among the top in the mid-Atlantic region for effectiveness of care.

DEAN ECKENRODE: *Integrated delivery, with financing and care giving, is not exactly unique. But a successful provider-based insurance company has never before been done in an academic medical environment. We haven't reached the pinnacle yet.*

Leaving Home: UPMC and the University Separate

As UPMC began to grow its integrated health delivery and financing model, the organization and its parent, the University of Pittsburgh, also took a fresh look at their own evolving relationship. With managed care plans penalizing academic medical centers and Congress anticipating a further $115 billion reduction in Medicare and Medicaid payments, universities around the country were re-evaluating their role in the management of teaching hospitals. "Academic medical centers have found themselves to be ill-fitted for the tightened belts of modern medicine," *The Chronicle of Higher Education* would report.

UPMC by 1997 consisted of a hospital system and subsidiary corporations organized into four operating divisions: Hospital, Physician, Insurance, and Diversified Services. University of Pittsburgh Chancellor Mark A. Nordenberg, former dean of the School of Law, recognized that the university and this large and complex "child" had outgrown their existing management contract. "Ultimately I thought that [the contract] just did not reflect the realities," Chancellor Nordenberg stated in 2005.

The university decided in 1997 to divest itself of its responsibilities related to UPMC. Once again relying on the changed governance model, the two organizations became separate entities, yet intertwined through board representation. The university dissolved its UPMC Division, and on July 1, 1998, the division's administrators became full-time employees of UPMC, reporting directly to the UPMC Board of Directors.

THOMAS DETRE: *The high-level university administrators were terrified, of course, of the potential economic downfall of the medical center, because one teaching hospital after another [around the country] went bankrupt. So they wanted to create a "fire wall," as I recall. It was really primarily for financial reasons, and, of course, those of us who were on the other side strongly urged the university to do that. That way we wouldn't have to be "constrained" by them.*

Pitt had a further motivation to separate from UPMC: The university had launched "the almost impossible challenge of finding a worthy successor to Dr. Detre," as Chancellor Nordenberg would put it in 2005.

Detre had first announced his intention to retire as senior vice chancellor in 1992. Two searches for his replacement had ended with no offer being made. Some said this was because of Romoff; a new senior vice chancellor would not want to play second fiddle to the forceful president of UPMC. Romoff recollects, "The notion was, I'm so strong, they could not hire the next Detre … having me in their midst."

Nordenberg diplomatically disagrees.

Dr. Detre first announced his intention to retire in 1992, but not until six years later did the University of Pittsburgh find a successor to its remarkable senior vice chancellor.

MARK NORDENBERG: *Jeff's principal responsibility was to the board of the health system, and while he had a line on the university's organizational chart to the chancellor, and he was respectful of the chancellor, still, his primary professional obligations were to the health system. And so in a lot of ways I really thought that the changes that we crafted were to bring the legal relationship into alignment with the realties in terms of management, and that actually was a pretty easy thing to do. I think there were times when Jeff may have thought that this also was a positive thing for me to do politically. I never viewed it that way. I really think I was looking at a person who was the CEO of a major organization who had a board, and in the end, what did that reporting line really mean if push came to shove?*

Marshall W. Webster, MD, executive vice president, UPMC; president, Physician Services Division; and chief medical officer

JEFFREY A. ROMOFF: *In any event, ultimately it liberated UPMC. It gave us enormous freedom!*

Putting Pieces Together: The Physician Practice Plans

The breakup of UPMC and the university went fairly smoothly except for one very contentious issue: the estimated millions of dollars a year in insurance reimbursements paid to the eighteen separate clinical practice plans composed of Pitt faculty physicians and dentists. UPMC and Pitt health sciences officials announced their intent to merge the practice plans into a not-for-profit subsidiary of UPMC that would "respond more efficiently to new opportunities in the health care market." UPMC would manage the practice plan fees and reimburse a negotiated amount each year to subsidize the schools of the health sciences. From UPMC's perspective this only made sense: UPMC already provided $50 million annually to the plans and subsidized as much as 40 percent of some medical school departments' budgets.

But this provision produced howls of protest from physicians fearing for their livelihoods and independence. They worried that "if UPMC and its dollar-focused leaders take control of medical school revenues, the school's core academic mission could suffer," according to the Pitt newspaper *University Times*. Discerning physicians also recognized that if UPMC controlled the flow of dollars, their compensation could eventually be tied to productivity.

"In the back of his head, [Jeffrey A. Romoff] felt that there were two components needed to make UPMC successful," suggests Dr. Marshall Webster, who became president of today's University of Pittsburgh Physicians (UPP), the multi-specialty practice group of the School of Medicine faculty. "The first component was the hospitals. The second was the physicians."

The clinical practice plans had originated in the 1970s as private practice corporations enabling School of Medicine faculty to bill patients and collect income apart from their university teaching salaries; they also subsidized the various departments of the School of Medicine. In addition to Dean Gerhard Werner, the leaders credited with engineering the plans were the medical school's stars of their day: Henry T. Bahnson, MD, chair of Surgery; Albert B. Ferguson Jr., MD, chair of Orthopaedic Surgery; and Jack D. Myers, MD, chair of Medicine. Although the university had tried to resist, these influential doctors argued that if the university wanted top-quality faculty, the clinical practice plan model was the way to go.

By 1997 "each practice plan was a fiefdom," declares George Huber. Each was a separate corporation with its own guidelines or bylaws, its own billing systems, its own fringe benefits, and its own compensation standards.

"In the past, when an outside entity like a health insurer wanted to contract with us, they had to deal with eighteen individual practice plan chairs plus the hospitals," said Dr. George K. Michalopoulos, who then served as associate vice chancellor for the Health Sciences and interim dean of the medical school. "By gathering all the clinical practice plans into one entity, we will make it easier for the plans to respond with one voice."

"The survival of the academic health center depends on its developing core competencies to manage clinical resources and complex, integrated, multi-institutional networks."

— National Conference of the University Hospital Consortium, February 1995

Not a single department chair wanted this merger. Faculty members charged that most of them had been excluded from the design of the proposed UPP. They decried a "Darth Vader" atmosphere. They complained that a UPMC "takeover of the Pitt practice plans would threaten to create a system that rewards faculty only for generating clinical revenue, thus undermining the medical school's teaching and research." (At about the same time, some faculty had also denounced what they saw as Senior Vice Chancellor Detre's policy of rewarding researchers at the *expense* of clinical care and teaching.) The president of the university senate wrote in the *University Times* that "despite its close links to the university at the board of trustees level, the UPMC Health System now appears to be more influenced by corporate managers, re-engineering consultants and money managers rather than by scholars, humanitarians and professionals selected by their peers who have long advocated accomplishment, dedication and ethical behavior in advancing medical care."

JULIUS YOUNGNER: *I watched the suffering that they went through with [creating] UPP – and the chairmen who bit the dust because they objected to it – but it was the way to go. It was ridiculous to have eighteen practice plans. And Tom and Jeff ended that. But it was a battle. It was a battle.*

[One day] there must have been an emergency because the executive committee, instead of meeting at the usual four o'clock, met at eight o'clock at night. Tom came in; he made an introduction and then turned the floor over to Jeffrey. And these chairmen, clinical chairmen, had all these arguments and facts. Jeff had more than they did. I was agog at how he had facts. And he just decimated their arguments, one after one. He took them to the cleaners – by logic, not by force.

As Jeff said to the chairmen that day, "If we don't do it, it's dog-eat-dog. If we don't do it, somebody else will. So we're going to do it."

After almost a year the cease-fire came suddenly, with UPMC posing as a dove bearing an olive branch the faculty could not refuse. UPMC offered to reimburse the practice plans for the $17 million they had been ordered to pay to federal and state governments to settle charges that Pitt physicians had overbilled Medicare and Medicaid between 1990 and 1996. The University of Pittsburgh was among the first of several medical teaching institutions to be audited by the Office of Inspector General for "compliance with rules governing physicians at teaching hospitals (PATH) and other Medicare payment rules." Although the universities maintained that the guidelines were vague and inconsistent, and at least one physician considered the government audits "extortion," the University of Pittsburgh negotiated a settlement in order to avoid long, costly, and risky litigation.

The settlement also included a corporate integrity agreement with a critical proviso: The practice plans' billing offices had to consolidate. Bingo. UPMC paid the fine; UPMC became home to UPP.

Physicians and Managers Collaborate

University of Pittsburgh Physicians is among the largest multi-specialty physician practice plans in the United States. And UPP has been vital to UPMC's development, mainly because despite the fears of many academic physicians, UPMC leadership respects the academic mission.

ROBERT CINDRICH: *There are plenty of universities that would love to have the model that was created here. The university knows how to conduct research and how to manage research, and they're very good at it; but what we're good at is the clinical side. So those doctors, in addition to teaching, have to deliver services. When you deliver services, you produce a fee; when you have people in your hospital, you get reimbursed. Now, if you can turn that into profits, you can put that back into the medical school.*

UPMC, then and now, always has been here to support the University of Pittsburgh schools of the health sciences. That's our raison d'être. That money allows this medical school to be at the top. They can recruit; they can have top-flight facilities. We can have the absolute best equipment, the best operating rooms in the city. It's symbiotic.

Senior Vice President, UPMC and Chief Human Resources and Administrative Services Officer Gregory K. Peaslee

Gregory K. Peaslee, who set up and served as the first real executive director of the consolidated plans, maintains that with centralized management, "We have drastically improved

Sandra N. Danoff, senior vice president, UPMC and chief communications officer

the billing for all the doctors. Our doctors make significantly more money, inflation-adjusted, than they did before."

"The physicians are paid very well and have the pride of place of working in a world-class environment," adds Dr. Webster. "But [UPP] also controls quality in the system. I think the future isn't just concern about cost – the future is about quality and optimum medical care. They are related. So when you really control, you actually can leverage that to optimal care."

When the health system has "a measure of control over the faculty and their clinical roles," says Loren Roth, "this is one of the secrets of the enormous growth over the last five to six years, because faculty productivity has gone up enormously."

The creation of UPP thus became yet another way to implement paradigm shifts. One important change was in the ways physicians' offices schedule patient appointments. The focus in this process moved from physicians to patients.

Embedded in UPMC's culture was a belief that when people were sick or hurting or worried about their health, to keep them waiting weeks for a doctor's appointment was "cruel," believes Sandra Danoff.

SANDRA DANOFF: *So in 2004 we began collaborating with the department chairs on an access initiative so that patients could get appointments quicker. Although waiting times of months to see specialists at academic medical centers are not uncommon across the country, at UPMC the collaboration with physicians allowed us to take this on. Eighty-five percent of our practices now routinely offer appointments within three days. Not only are patients more satisfied, but also department chairmen view this initiative as empowering, because once their schedules started to fill, the productivity went up, and once the productivity went up, the revenues went up, and once the revenues went up, they gained funds to support recruitment, new programs, research – the elements that are central to academic excellence.*

A New Senior Vice Chancellor

Many believed the "firewall" between the University of Pittsburgh and UPMC would enable Pitt at last to end its six-year search for a new senior vice chancellor for the Health Sciences … someone with the vision, talent, and toughness to succeed Thomas Detre. To wide approval, the university announced the appointment of Arthur S. Levine, MD, as both senior vice chancellor and dean of the School of Medicine in May 1998. "Take him," Detre had urged the search committee within moments of meeting Dr. Levine. "Grab him," Romoff advised Chancellor Mark Nordenberg after spending an hour with Levine.

Arthur Levine came to Pittsburgh from a thirty-one-year career at the National Institutes of Health, where his primary focus was molecular biology. He had no ambition to manage or control the university-related hospitals. He said at the time that the Pittsburgh job "is more attractive to me because they put the hospital complex in the hands of people whose lifetime business it is to make [it] work with a degree of success and productivity."

ARTHUR LEVINE: *I became quite intrigued [with the University of Pittsburgh] because I realized quickly that this institution, which had been an average regional institution for a hundred years, suddenly had an inflection point. What was most impressive to me was the increase in federal funding for its research program, because that's really the only metric that we have in a nationally competitive peer-review context that examines anything about a medical school.*

Although there were other academic medical centers that were equally or more accomplished and had the same aspirations, I thought the rapidity with which this was happening was unique. This was, as far as I knew, the largest increase per unit of time in federal support for biomedical research of any institution in the country's modern history.

The multifaceted Arthur S. Levine, MD, succeeded Dr. Detre as senior vice chancellor in 1998. At the National Institutes of Health his research had focused on molecular biology.

Levine leveraged this success by expanding research at the University of Pittsburgh in the basic sciences.

MARK NORDENBERG: *Tom Detre always said that he had done as much to fuel the growth and progress of the university via the medical center as a psychiatrist could do, and that our next senior vice chancellor really needed to be someone who had a stronger grounding in basic biology; and, of course, Dr. Levine fits that description perfectly. And he has done a remarkable job of doing honor to Tom's legacy by building on it, and he and Jeff have a strong relationship, I would say, where they are very respectful of each other.*

ARTHUR LEVINE: *[Coming to Pittsburgh has] allowed me to do what I hoped to do, which is to build a kind of basic science that's most apt to eventuate in shifting the paradigm in health care, and also leading to the development of a biotechnology industry; and given my entrepreneurial bent, that was an interest of mine also.*

Children's Hospital, and a New Contract with Highmark

By 2001 UPMC controlled 42 percent of the hospital beds in Allegheny County. Years of collaboration were formalized as Magee-Womens Hospital and Children's Hospital of Pittsburgh, the last independent hospitals in the original university medical center system, joined UPMC, Magee-Womens in 1999 and Children's in 2001. The merger with Children's, western Pennsylvania's only tertiary pediatric hospital, proved especially bumpy.

Although Children's shared services and projects with UPMC, the hospital had insisted on maintaining an independent governance. In 2000, however, Children's faced the need to replace century-old facilities. Senior Vice Chancellor Arthur Levine had joined the Children's board, recalls Roger A. Oxendale, CEO of Children's Hospital from 2005–2009. "He right away was talking about research and the fact that if we were going to be anything compared to any other children's hospital, we needed to ramp up our research program even more, and we would need more space." Oxendale came to the hospital from AHERF in 1995 as chief financial officer. He and Ronald L. Violi, a business entrepreneur who was the chairman of the Children's board and later served as its president and CEO, had put the hospital on a firmer financial footing.

Roger A. Oxendale, former CEO, Children's Hospital of Pittsburgh of UPMC and president, Children's Hospital Foundation

But Children's also felt threatened by UPMC's new control of the clinical faculty through UPP. If the hospital didn't toe the line, would UPMC tell the physicians they couldn't practice there? "I told our CEO at the time that whoever controls the physicians really controls Children's," says Oxendale in characteristically calm, measured tones. "So I think what began to become very clear to the board is that we really weren't independent of UPMC. We were very much integrated already."

That recognition prompted a dinner meeting at the Duquesne Club with Violi, Oxendale, Jeffrey A. Romoff, and John Paul. They agreed they could work out a deal. After a "long, emotional, dramatic board meeting" (some board members viewed UPMC as the evil empire), Children's accepted UPMC's offer to build a new hospital, along with an additional $25 million a year for the next decade toward researchers, new research facilities, and expanded programs. Romoff believed UPMC could make Children's a much stronger hospital by applying the model of integrated research, teaching, and clinical care.

"A firestorm of questions" broke out when Children's and UPMC signed a letter of intent to merge in April 2001. Many feared that the hospital, so beloved in Pittsburgh, would become a pawn in the ongoing battles between UPMC and Highmark Inc.

MAGEE-WOMENS HOSPITAL

CHILDREN'S HOSPITAL OF PITTSBURGH

Years of collaboration were formalized as Magee-Womens Hospital and Children's Hospital of Pittsburgh joined UPMC.

Highmark and others threatened that Children's costs would rise and that UPMC would lock out non-UPP physicians. Highmark filed a federal lawsuit to prevent the merger on antitrust grounds – and at the same time offered Children's up to $250 million to finance a new facility if the hospital would stay independent of UPMC.

"Com*plete*ly wrong," Romoff told the *Pittsburgh Post-Gazette* editorial board about Highmark's antitrust charges. UPMC, he said, had no intention of using its control of Children's to gain an unfair advantage for its UPMC Health Plan.

Also working to avert the UPMC–Children's merger was the new West Penn Allegheny Health System, a network formed after the collapse of AHERF in 1998. To save Allegheny General Hospital and its suburban Pittsburgh affiliates from bankruptcy, Highmark had provided financial backing for their merger with the West Penn Health System. UPMC, not surprisingly, had viewed Highmark's $125 million loan "as a backdoor through which Highmark could ultimately take control" of the new system. UPMC had lobbied publicly against it, challenging the amount a health insurer's financial reserves could be invested in a single business venture. Now, with UPMC about to take over management and governance of Children's, it was Highmark's turn to fire a few shots across the bow. Highmark withdrew its lawsuit, however, when the UPMC–Children's merger received the state attorney general's approval.

UPMC/Highmark hostilities festered over the following months, just when the two were trying to forge a critical new long-term contract. Representing 24 percent of UPMC's revenue, Highmark subscribers were must-haves for the system. Without a new Highmark contract, bond ratings agencies threatened to lower UPMC's rating.

Nevertheless, Romoff had no hesitation about taking Highmark to the mat. "Taking on a Goliath is a real opportunity for UPMC," he always believed. And John Paul, who was negotiating for UPMC, "was always a brinksman, which created a lot of tension for the rest of us," George Huber recalls. "He was an outstanding negotiator."

The insurer demanded UPMC's best prices; UPMC countered that its reimbursements had dropped 21 percent when adjusted for inflation and it had received no Highmark increases for six years. UPMC demanded higher reimbursements to support the academic medical mission. Of course, Highmark needed UPMC's hospitals, too, and UPMC threatened to end its contracts with Highmark unless the insurer also contributed to the building of a new Children's Hospital. "Extortion," Highmark called this.

Rumors abounded that UPMC's rising debt and a sinking stock market were causing the system to rethink its original offer to Children's. UPMC denied this. On a taped local television show, Jeffrey A. Romoff accused Highmark of being a "ticket scalper," charging higher and higher premiums while its cash reserves swelled to $2.3 billion. Highmark retorted that the growth in its reserves had come from investment income, not premium income. Newspapers characterized the contract dispute as "King Kong vs. Godzilla" or compared the two to sumo wrestlers bumping bellies.

On June 26, 2002, four days before their contract expired, UPMC and Highmark reached a new ten-year agreement. UPMC gained price increases, while Highmark won continued access for its subscribers to nearly all the region's doctors and hospitals. "We actually signed on June 30, 2002," says David Farner. "It came down to the wire."

Two months later UPMC and Highmark reconciled, at the deathbed of financially troubled St. Francis Hospital. The 137-year-old hospital, located about two miles from Oakland, was about to close. "Why not come together in a community-spirited proposal and rescue St. Francis' flagship medical center as a new home for Children's Hospital?" UPMC suggested to Highmark.

"Right after the contract got signed, John Paul was saying we ought to do this jointly with Highmark, we have to bail out St. Francis," recalls Tal Heppenstall. "An investment banker from Goldman Sachs said, 'You're crazy. Let it go bankrupt and you can get it for ten cents on the dollar.'

"'Nope. That's not what we're doing,' was UPMC's response."

Why not?

"They believed that the community would suffer from another health care bankruptcy," Heppenstall says. "It wasn't good for the employees, and it wasn't good for the patients, and it wasn't good for the physicians. Or for the sisters." The Sisters of St. Francis had established the hospital just after the civil war.

The St. Francis resolution offered a "graceful conclusion" to the acrimony. Pittsburgh Bishop Donald Wuerl, while regretting the end of St. Francis Hospital, said that the opening of a new Children's Hospital on the site would be "a blessing for the whole community."

The bishop, recalled Ralph Cappy, had final sign-off authority on the transfer of the St. Francis property to UPMC. "You can't get it approved by Rome unless the bishop approves," he explained.

RALPH CAPPY: *I had represented to the bishop that in my twenty years of experience with Jeff Romoff and John Paul, I had never seen either of them ever break their word, even sometimes when it was to their detriment. If they shook your hand, that was it.*

He was willing to accept that, but I said, "Don't you think it's a good idea that you actually get to know Jeffrey Romoff? You should be comfortable knowing that if Jeffrey speaks publicly about this potential merger and this mission, that it's consistent with your view, and that it won't complicate your life with Rome and the sisters."

So we go to dinner at the bishop's house. And it was just remarkable. Bishop Wuerl is a very refined man. He speaks six or seven languages; he is an historian in the true sense of the academic word. Well, these two get together, and you would have thought they had known each other for thirty years. They're off on some discussion about the history of some obscure place that they both knew about ... this is a train that's definitely going in the right direction. At the end of the dinner the two of them stand up – during the course of this discussion they had talked of the needs of the Catholic Church and the bishop's needs particularly so he could get Rome to sign off, and Jeffrey explained what he felt was appropriate and what he thought he could get his board to do. They shook hands, and I'll be darned if what they agreed on that night wasn't actually consummated with all the legalities later on. Remarkable.

A dinner with Bishop Donald Wuerl (above) and Jeffrey A. Romoff cleared the way for UPMC to build a new Children's Hospital on the site of the former St. Francis Hospital.

As the *Pittsburgh Post-Gazette* concluded in August 2002, "The convergence of interests that will enable southwestern Pennsylvania's largest hospital chain, using money from the region's largest health insurer, to ... rebuild [St. Francis] as a state-of-the-art Children's Hospital – is a profound event in regional health care."

Planning for the new hospital went forward. After a while, though, some members of the Children's board decided that UPMC "was not living up to its end of the bargain," Roger Oxendale recollects.

ROGER OXENDALE: *The words in the document stated there would be a world-class, state-of-the-art hospital, and our interpretation of the language was that it was regardless of the price. UPMC didn't share that point of view. They felt ... a reasonable-man provision needed to come into this, that we couldn't just spend however much money we wanted. But I think all of us were underestimating what it was really going to take to build a new hospital.*

During a "difficult" board meeting, Oxendale and two others were dispatched to Chancellor Nordenberg's office to alert him that "we were going to blow this whole thing up." The chancellor asked them to give him a couple of days to "get clarification on this," Oxendale remembers. But at the conclusion of the board meeting, unbeknownst to the three meeting with Nordenberg, hospital president and CEO Ronald Violi had decided to take the dispute to the media. After months of public rancor, though, UPMC and Children's agreed on a cap figure for the new hospital.

Children's Hospital of Pittsburgh of UPMC, Imaging Waiting Area

ROGER OXENDALE: *And so that really began our next phase of our journey, which was to build a great Children's Hospital and continue to develop the great services that we have had here in Oakland. There have been some other, more minor challenges, but we've faced them together.*

In 2007 the chair of the Children's board, Mary Jo Dively, vice president and general counsel of Carnegie Mellon University, said, "It would be very hard for anyone to argue that UPMC is not putting enough money into this hospital. They've done everything they said they would do."

The new Children's Hospital of Pittsburgh of UPMC would officially open its 1.5-million-square-foot, state-of-the-art hospital on a ten-acre campus on May 2, 2009.

Mercy Hospital: "A Great Honor to Join in Your Ministry"

UPMC now includes Pittsburgh's newest hospital as well as its very first. In 1843, seven Sisters of Mercy arrived in Pittsburgh from Ireland and on January 1, 1847, opened the order's first hospital in the United States, as well as the first nonmilitary hospital in Pittsburgh. From that moment The Mercy Hospital became a "pillar of Pittsburgh," entwined in the lives of generations of families. "It was a place where Rooneys came into the world and a place where they said goodbye," write Arthur J. Rooney Jr. and Roy McHugh in *Ruanaidh: The Story of Art Rooney and His Clan.* Pittsburghers rich and poor could say the same.

By the early 2000s, 535-bed Mercy Hospital's financial problems concerned and saddened many. To compete, Pittsburgh's last Catholic hospital would need to invest at least $60 million in physicians and equipment. But its parent, Catholic Health East, "really didn't think they could afford to invest that kind of money," remembers John R. McGinley Jr., who chaired Mercy's board. Everyone involved, especially Sister Margaret Hannan, RSM, president of the Pittsburgh Regional Community of the Sisters of Mercy of the Americas, felt the urgent necessity to preserve the institution's historic legacy, retain its Catholic identity, and continue Mercy's work in the low-income and vulnerable communities the hospital served. "We conducted a thoughtful, inclusive, and innovative process to ensure the future of Mercy Hospital," Sister Hannan would write. "Pittsburgh Mercy Health System searched all possible alternatives."

UPMC Director John R. McGinley Jr. served as chair of The Mercy Hospital of Pittsburgh board.

McGinley remembers that Bishop Donald Wuerl, who in 2006 would become Archbishop of Washington, DC, "sent a message that we shouldn't be afraid to talk to Jeffrey Romoff if we need some help." UPMC had already assisted Mercy with staffing "when West Penn made a run on our anesthesiologists."

A member of the law firm Eckert Seamans, Jack McGinley was a longtime friend of Robert Cindrich, UPMC's chief legal officer. "I didn't know Jeffrey personally," McGinley says, "but everybody who I felt knew anything about the situation said the guy was first-class – tough, but you could take his word to the bank. And any place that has Bob working there has to be OK.

"All of those things matter to me. So I called Bob."

JOHN MCGINLEY: *Truth be told, I took him fishing. He's a fisherman, and I'm a fisherman. I needed to get him away from telephones, so I took him up to Spruce Creek. And the next day, as we were wrapping up, I said to him, "How's the hospital business, Bob?"*

"Oh, we're doing great," he said. "How are things at Mercy?"
And I said, "I think we can use some help."

"What kind of help are you thinking of?" he asked. And I said, "I'm not quite sure. But we want to retain our Catholic identity institutionally."

In an hour and a half, in a trout stream, the seeds were planted for Mercy Hospital's affiliation with UPMC.

Catholic health care speaks to spiritual as well as physical needs. According to the Diocese of Pittsburgh, "There is one fundamental commandment for a Catholic hospital: All life, from conception to the moment of natural death, is profoundly sacred. All life must therefore be treated with awe, respect, and dignity. This fundamental commandment comes without a 'but,' 'if,' or 'however.' There is no qualification, no exception."

Sister Margaret Hannan invited Romoff, Cindrich, McGinley, and others to a meeting at the Sisters of Mercy motherhouse in Oakland. She opened the meeting with a prayer, then laid out the situation. Without help, Mercy would have to close. If UPMC would be interested in assuming the sponsorship of Mercy Hospital, she thought that that could be appropriate.

"What do you need?" Romoff asked.

"One hundred million to continue," was the answer.

"OK," he replied. "Now we'll work it out."

McGinley describes the ensuing negotiations as "extremely professional, direct, and we never, to my recollection, had a major business disagreement on any material term." On September 20, 2006, the Pittsburgh Mercy Health System and its parent

"At UPMC we always have a sense of needing to be better," asserts Jeffrey A. Romoff. "Every time I get to the top of a mountain, I see another mountain that is higher."

organization, Catholic Health East, announced that they had signed a letter of intent to transfer ownership of The Mercy Hospital of Pittsburgh to UPMC. Mercy would continue as a Catholic hospital, with canonical oversight from the diocese.

Included in the agreement was a $100 million contribution from UPMC to a charitable fund to be administered by the Sisters of Mercy. Sister Hannan said the fund would be used to enhance programs for the poor and meet other community needs. Robert Cindrich also pointed out that UPMC's investment in Mercy would help "revitalize downtown Pittsburgh."

"While some may look at UPMC's Mercy acquisition as a mere extension of the health care giant's growing empire, others saw the hand of God at work, particularly given Mercy's financial struggles," a Pittsburgh newspaper article would state. West Penn Allegheny Health System, however, raised questions about a "medical monopoly." Not until May 2007 did Pennsylvania Attorney General Tom Corbett give approval for the merger – with the stipulation that both the Federal Trade Commission (FTC) and the Vatican also had to approve it. During this time, Mercy Hospital continued to deteriorate. The FTC dragged its heels until the appointment in July 2007 of the new bishop of Pittsburgh, David A. Zubik. When Bishop Zubik met with Jeffrey A. Romoff, the UPMC president indicated that the Mercy deal would have to move faster; the hospital was losing value every day.

"And after that, I would say that Bishop Zubik went to work," Jack McGinley comments. "He energized and really catalyzed the FTC effort. He was the agent of an approval in time for us to get the transaction done." After reviewing tens of thousands of documents, the FTC cleared the transfer of ownership in October 2007. One month later, the Vatican gave its approval.

On January 1, 2008, the first day of Mercy's 161st year of service, the hospital officially became part of UPMC. The Mercy community marked the historic event with "a celebration of remembrance, thanksgiving, and transition" in the hospital's

From left, John R. McGinley Jr.; Sister Margaret Hannan, RSM; Bishop David A. Zubik; and Jeffrey A. Romoff at "a celebration of remembrance, thanksgiving, and transition," January 3, 2008

The Mercy Hospital of Pittsburgh was the first hospital opened by the Sisters of Mercy in the United States. Today, UPMC Mercy is the only faith-based hospital in the Pittsburgh region.

Holy Family Chapel. Romoff praised Mercy, saying, "You have taken a 160-year tradition of excellence, of commitment, you have taken a contemporary situation of great difficulty in a difficult world, and you have managed to find a way to transition that to preserve the best of what you have built and to trust it to someone else in a most modern of ways while losing nothing of the spirit."

He said he was moved by Sister Margaret Hannan's invitation to UPMC to join in the ministry of the Sisters of Mercy.

"If joining in the ministry means sustaining the highest quality care for our citizens, if joining in the ministry means respecting and honoring and following the edicts of Catholic health care, if joining in the ministry means serving this community, the poor as well as the rich, and if joining in the ministry means doing that in such a fashion that we can be both charitable and successful, then I can only say that it is a great honor to join in your ministry," he concluded.

"The reason UPMC is successful is because we always have a sense of needing to be better. Leverage, leverage, leverage. You develop a technology, then what does that mean? How can you use it? What is the marketplace for that thing?"

— Jeffrey A. Romoff

From Pittsburgh to Palermo: transplanting technology and building a platform for a new vision

1996 UPMC and the Italian government sign a letter of intent for UPMC to develop the *Istituto Mediterraneo per i Trapianti e Terapie ad Alta Specializzazione* (the Mediterranean Institute for Transplantation and Highly Specialized Therapies), known as ISMETT. It is the first public-private partnership ever developed in Sicily.

1999 ISMETT's first organ transplant is performed in Palermo on July 30.

2000 *The Wall Street Journal* describes ISMETT as "currently the most ambitious international effort by a U.S. medical center."

2004 ISMETT's new, seventy-bed hospital opens.

2006 ISMETT performs more than a hundred transplants each year, along with specialized medical procedures never before offered in southern Italy.

The UPMC Whitfield Cancer Centre opens in Waterford, Ireland.

UPMC signs a five-year, $100 million contract to provide emergency medical services in Qatar.

2007 UPMC begins operating the Beacon Cancer Centre at Beacon Hospital in Dublin, Ireland.

2008 UPMC announces an agreement to manage the Beacon Hospital in Dublin.

2009 UPMC signs an agreement to create the Biomedical Research and Biotechnology Center in Sicily.

1996–2009

Whitfield Clinic, Waterford, Ireland, home of UPMC Whitfield Cancer Centre

8

A Culture of Hunger

*"If we develop a technology of excellence here in Pittsburgh – the most sophisticated clinical care that there is – and are able to develop the capacity to export it, we have created a commodity of enormous value. Of **enormous** value."* — Jeffrey A. Romoff

Amid formative, combative years of nonstop mergers, acquisitions, integrations, and construction, few organizations feel pressured simultaneously to develop yet another, different future. But in the 1990s the young UPMC began to reimagine its advanced clinical care and management strengths as technology that could be leveraged and exported beyond the bounds of its traditional markets in western Pennsylvania.

Within less than a decade and in spite of unique challenges and barriers, these explorations would lead to the first American organ transplant center in Europe, and the largest in Italy. They would lead to the establishment of cancer centers and hospital management in Ireland, emergency medical services in Qatar, and information technology transfer in the United Kingdom. They would transform UPMC's sense of its own possibilities.

In 2006 Congressman John P. Murtha (right) announced that UPMC had received $8.5 million from the House Appropriations Subcommittee on Defense to build the Strategic Biodefense Emergency Operations and Communications System (SBEOCS).

Culture of Hunger, Culture of Becoming

UPMC's international expansion illustrates the relentless drive that characterizes this unusual health system. Without question, it's a culture created by powerful personalities, leaders with a voracious appetite to excel. As Congressman John P. Murtha of Pennsylvania says, "They have a vision which is driven from the top. And I would say it's a world-class organization."

JEFFREY A. ROMOFF: *Organizations that want to continue to be great need to have a sense of hunger. If you're not hungry, if you don't have a sense of needing to accomplish something, then I think you diminish the energy of the organization, you diminish the commitment of the organization, you diminish the arousal of the organization. Organizations must be aroused in order to mobilize.*

Organizations must be attentive, ready to leverage and focus their resources when the external environment and their internal capabilities change, Romoff believes. "The reason UPMC is successful is because we keep moving the ball," he asserts. "We always have a sense of needing to be better.

"Leverage, leverage, leverage," he reiterates. "You develop a technology, then what does that mean? How can you use it? What is the marketplace for that thing?" Romoff's UPMC is "always becoming."

But anyone who assumes UPMC changes simply to expand the boundaries of its "empire" misses the point.

JEFFREY A. ROMOFF: *If change is only incremental, it ends up only with an incremental end. And it just becomes one more brick in the house on top of the hill. We don't want another brick in the house on top of the hill. We just jumped off a hill, we're at the bottom of another hill, and now we need climbing shoes, guides, and compasses!*

In the punishing process of learning how to export its programs into new countries and cultures, UPMC entered a new phase in its coming of age. "This departure, this international programming, is of enormous significance," Romoff states. "UPMC's international expansion is the distillation of all that we do. We built our future around the core issues entailed in getting this done."

A Life of Border Crossings

"In today's world," Thomas Detre often said, "you cannot establish your reputation if it doesn't go beyond the Pittsburgh airport. If you really want to make it, you have to be, ultimately, internationally known." From Kecskemét to Budapest to Rome to New Haven to Pittsburgh, Detre's own life was a series of border crossings. Nationality never stood in the way of his vision to bring the best people to Pittsburgh and to build a great academic medical center.

THOMAS DETRE: *Even at WPIC I felt that when you recruit, you do not compromise, and you cannot be so provincial as to say that we will not get a leader for a program unless the applicant is American. In today's world that doesn't mean a damned thing. I thought that the best person should get the job, and for that reason I always wanted to have intelligent young men and women come and work with us here, and then spread the news abroad that we are not a provincial institution, and anybody who wants to come here to work or study is welcome.*

Like all top academicians, Dr. Detre traveled abroad to lecture and teach. He consulted at the highest levels. He had "a good working relationship," for instance, with President Süleyman Demirel of Turkey. Detre advised the president on the development of medical science in Turkish hospitals, and Turkish physicians came to Pittsburgh as fellows.

From left, Jeffrey A. Romoff, Thomas Detre, MD, Pittsburgh Mayor Tom Murphy, and University of Pittsburgh Chancellor Mark A. Nordenberg on their way to greet Süleyman Demirel, president of Turkey

THOMAS DETRE: *There were big luncheons given in my honor in Turkey – in the presidential palace with ministers, army chiefs, you name it. The fact that I was just a guest and did not have any political agenda pleased them no end because they were not used to that. I was interested in their views. I was interested in how the country functions, how they were doing their jobs, how Turkey compares to the United States or Italy or Hungary, things like that.*

When Turkish President Süleyman Demirel (center) received an honorary degree from the University of Pittsburgh, he and his wife were welcomed to the city by Thomas Detre, MD (left), Jeffrey A. Romoff (hidden), and Mark A. Nordenberg (left of President Demirel).

Detre thus won friends for Pittsburgh: wealthy Turkish citizens began coming to the medical center for health care "in fairly large numbers." And, because of the worldwide quest for health – and the diplomatic advantage of medical education over military force – he became a sort of ambassador without portfolio for the United States.

One day Detre got a call from a physician in Saudi Arabia. "They wanted to create a modern psychiatric service," he recalls. "Would I come as a consultant?

"'Of course, it would be a pleasure,' I said. 'But I want you to know that I am a Jew.'

"'Oh, that doesn't matter at all,' they replied," somewhat to his surprise.

At the same time, members of the Saudi royal family came to Pittsburgh to benefit from Thomas Starzl's world-leading organ transplant program, and Starzl also visited Saudi Arabia.

"There was, of course, a controversy associated with this," Detre recalls, "because people were complaining about why these Saudi princes were getting organs when U.S. citizens weren't." At this point Detre, then Pitt's senior vice chancellor for the Health Sciences, received another surprising telephone call – from the Reagan Administration. "The White House asked us if we could be 'helpful,'" he recounts, in continuing to care for the Saudis.

THOMAS DETRE: *My view was a little broader [than the controversy over U.S. versus foreign transplants]. If the Saudis are doing us a favor by mitigating oil prices, we owe them something. Maybe not love, but if they need our help, we should give them some help. You know, they were somewhat dubious but important allies of this country.*

When the White House asked us if we could be helpful, I thought, well, that's perfectly legitimate. We are not talking here about money. We are talking here about maintaining cordial relationships. It is natural that if somebody who is important to the country gets sick, we will try to take care of him. That's in the best national interest.

His Excellency Ismail Sallam of Egypt believes that "health diplomacy" could be a potent force against terrorism. "Health touches the heart," he says simply. "Health could bring the world together."

There is no more fervent spokesman for health as diplomacy than His Excellency Ismail Sallam, a cardiac surgeon and former minister of Health and Population for Egypt. Professor Sallam believes passionately that health care and education can alleviate social and economic disparities. He also believes that "health diplomacy" could be a potent force against terrorism. "Health touches the heart," he says simply. "Health could bring the world together." When he asked UPMC to help him develop a center of excellence for heart surgery, Detre went to Cairo.

THOMAS DETRE: *I rarely get astonished, but he astonished me. I chatted with him for about an hour; then he took me by the arm and led me into his cabinet meeting, and said, "Now here is somebody you should really be listening to. Here is somebody who can do some good."*

UPMC regularly sent surgeons, cardiologists, and nurses to train Egyptians, and to follow up this training with continuing critiques and monitoring inside the operating room and in intensive care.

UPMC also tried to establish programs in several South American countries during the 1980s and 1990s. However, neither there nor in Cairo were these efforts lastingly successful. Establishing a beachhead in Egypt was not "timely," Detre says. There were simply too many cultural and economic hurdles to overcome. And UPMC was determined to export what it considered Pittsburgh standards. "We are different from other academic medical centers who have gone abroad," claims Charles E. Bogosta, executive vice president, UPMC; executive vice president, UPMC Cancer Centers; and president, International and Commercial Services Division. "Others show up with a logo and some junior fellows. We show up with a SWAT team."

Charles E. Bogosta, executive vice president, UPMC; executive vice president, UPMC Cancer Centers; and president, International and Commercial Services Division

But in another equally complex part of the world, UPMC did prevail, and this success has permanently altered the hopes and rugged landscape of Sicily, the largest island in the Mediterranean Sea. In Sicily's capital, Palermo, UPMC has built the *Istituto Mediterraneo per i Trapianti e Terapie ad Alta Specializzazione* (the Mediterranean Institute for Transplantation and Highly Specialized Therapies), known as ISMETT. The first public-private partnership ever developed in Sicily, ISMETT provides lifesaving organ transplants and other advanced medical procedures previously unavailable to the people of southern Italy. In addition, the institute is becoming a referral center for other Mediterranean and Middle East countries.

Not surprisingly, "Palermo was a perfect microcosm of all the kinds of oppositional, combative resistance that UPMC in fact faced here in the United States," Romoff recalls. "We would have been snuffed out when we went to Palermo – if we hadn't trained for Palermo here at home."

At right, the Cathedral of Palermo, Cattedrale dall'alto

Leveraging

"If we want everything to remain as it is, it will be necessary for everything to change," wrote Sicily's most famous novelist, Giuseppe Tomasi di Lampedusa, in *The Leopard.* ("*Se vogliamo che tutto rimanga com'è bisogna che tutto cambi.*") Change has never come easily to this mountainous, history-steeped island off the toe of the Italian boot, notorious in popular imagination for its insularity, resistance to authority, and the Mafia.

In 1995 Sicily was a region with five million people and not one organ transplant facility. "From Naples downward," Thomas Detre confirms, "there was no really comprehensive transplant center that functioned well." Seriously ill Sicilians were forced to make "*viaggi di speranza*" (voyages of hope) to northern Italy or to countries outside Italy, undergoing life-threatening surgical procedures far from home and the support of beloved families. Each year the University of Palermo's Hospital Cervello sent dozens of patients abroad for transplants; these desperate journeys were costing the Sicilian government an estimated $170 million a year.

Meanwhile, five thousand miles away, UPMC had created the most active organ transplant programs in the world, but patients from outside the U.S. were losing their chance to benefit from these resources. The United Network for Organ Sharing (UNOS), a private group with the contract to administer the national Organ Procurement and Transportation Network, had ruled to limit "nonresident alien"

UPMC was able to help people in Italy and other parts of the world by building on the organ transplantation programs of Thomas E. Starzl, MD, PhD, who was named a 2004 National Medal of Science laureate, the nation's highest scientific honor, "for his pioneering work in liver transplantation and his discoveries in immunosuppressive medications that advanced the field of organ transplantation."

recipients to 10 percent of donated organs. By 1992 UNOS was considering whether to lower this limit to 5 percent, a proposal that threatened UPMC's ability to serve international patients and to cut into an important revenue stream.

But Jeffrey A. Romoff denies that declining reimbursement and problems with organ allocations were UPMC's major motivations for exporting its programs. "We could live with a hundred fewer liver transplants," he insists. "If UPMC wanted to be a successful organization, it needed to leverage and to use what had already been done."

The door to exporting UPMC's expertise in transplantation to Sicily opened at a 1995 medical conference in Rome when an Italian-born transplant surgeon on Starzl's team met with a liver specialist and chairman of medicine at the University of Palermo. That university's Cervello Hospital was Sicily's largest referral center for liver disease. The two discussed UPMC's capabilities and the needs of Italian medical care. The Palermo physician invited UPMC transplant surgeons to come to Sicily.

Thomas Detre, MD (center), receiving one of his many honors in Italy.

To Thomas Detre and Jeffrey A. Romoff, Italy seemed what Detre called "a logical place" to put down European roots.

THOMAS DETRE: *For me Italy had sentimental value because I can't tell you how cordial, decent, and friendly my colleagues were in Italy when I arrived there [in 1947] without speaking a word of Italian. Everybody rushed to my aid, literally everybody. I had a strong sense of gratitude. And I really hoped that one day we would do something together.*

There were many patients coming from Italy, and so Jeff and I started to roam the country to see where it could be established; and then the Sicilian government was interested.

The Sicilian government was indeed interested. Palermo's mayor, Leoluca Orlando, was promoting a "Palermo Renaissance." He realized that better health care could help revitalize his city – and, with his reputation as an anti-Mafia reformer, he saw foreign ventures as an opportunity to loosen the grip of organized crime. "I was happy when McDonald's came to Palermo," he would tell *The Wall Street Journal* in 2000. "So imagine how happy I am that [UPMC] has come to Palermo."

Cardinal Salvatore Pappalardo, former Archbishop of Palermo, also would use his influence to help UPMC start a transplant center. The first Sicilian churchman to break the local *omertà*, or code of silence, to speak out against the Mafia, Cardinal Pappalardo spoke out as well in favor of organ donations, calling them "a gesture of ... Christian solidarity and charity." Yet another factor in UPMC's favor was a new

Italian law, *Sperimentazione Gestionale*, which for the first time allowed the national government to help fund new enterprises and new businesses in various regions of Italy, including Sicily.

So the circumstantial evidence seemed to favor UPMC's transferring medical services to Palermo. Yet "Palermo was a unique set of challenges, and fairly serious challenges," recalls Romoff, "challenges that have made what we do in Palermo literally unique in the world."

Desire and Resistance in Palermo

The primary barrier was the obvious one: Sicily was a foreign culture with its own timeless, ingrained, unwritten rules, conflicts, jealousies, and hierarchies.

Cardinal Salvatore Pappalardo

JEFFREY A. ROMOFF: *Americans don't understand foreign cultures. And what is worse, they don't want to understand foreign cultures. And worse than that, they don't want to recognize that they exist. Foreign cultures are challenging, particularly in the area of health care.*

Health care is a significant, visible, public issue. Because European health care is mostly government-driven, governments are defined by the success or failure of health care. The regional government in Sicily changed seven times in ten years. The national government changed three times. It's hard to establish neutrality and credibility in that situation, to walk that fine line.

Health care in Italy, as in America, is an esteemed discipline, and physicians are powerful. Everything that you bring that portends to bring something better – which is the only reason anyone would pay you to be there – threatens the existing system. And those people who feel threatened are powerful, and, most importantly, they understand the culture in a way you will never understand it.

I'm not exaggerating this. And to the extent that you get government support, you get significant opposition from the other party, whatever it is.

Cardinal Achille Silvestrini (center), a prominent Vatican diplomat, introduced his friend Thomas Detre, MD (right), to Pope Benedict XVI (left) in 2005.

You get opposition from the community, because there are always hospitals that have not been blessed with the kinds of resources that we have gotten, so they say, "Why does this bunch of foreigners come in here and get hundreds of millions of dollars when we live in a hell-hole of a hospital?" That is a very potent argument. It is the argument for the status quo. It is always the argument for the status quo.

Italy, in fact, falls into last place in Europe for direct investment from the United States – precisely because businesspeople complain about the difficulties of navigating "a complicated culture of rules – those broken, as well as those impossible to understand," according to *The New York Times*. "Faced with greedy and hostile authority over many chaotic centuries, it is argued, Italians fell back into the idea that only the family can be trusted."

And as Luigi Barzini writes in *The Italians*, "If most Italians manage at times to weave skillfully in and out of written laws, most Sicilians appear to avoid them all completely. The simplest project, something which could be carried out anywhere else by means of a letter and a couple of conversations, becomes among Sicilians an enterprise of heroic proportions, each participant inventing diabolical schemes of his own to get the better of his opponent and, at the same time, foresee all possible schemes which his opponent will try to employ."

Is it any wonder that UPMC's challenge-driven leaders were attracted to Sicily?

Thomas Detre believes that "desire and resistance were simultaneously present" in Palermo. "I think that strange kind of ambivalence is understandable, given the culture," he says. "Islands tend to be somewhat insular. This insularity causes them to be more suspicious of change, and more leery of change.

"Nobody wants to change," he remarks with a very Italian shrug. "If somebody wants to change something around me, I wouldn't like it either, even though I was a change agent!"

On the other hand, didn't Sicilians want to help those forced to embark on *viaggi di speranza*?

THOMAS DETRE: *Yes. They knew [these trips were] very expensive; they knew it was inconvenient for the families; they knew that certain subspecialties were not present in Sicily. Of course, that's also some source of embarrassment. So in come the foreigners to do this? Why not Italians? Well, actually the Italians were reluctant to come to Sicily, because one of the strange things on that island is that everything becomes a game. It's too complicated.*

Romoff remembers that the UPMC board had serious discussions about the wisdom of establishing a transplant center in Sicily. "Understandably," he states. "Were we taking resources away from Pittsburgh?" Other medical centers' foreign ventures had been less than successful.

JEFFREY A. ROMOFF: *No one had made money doing this. No one had done it successfully, just like no one had done a health plan from a provider system successfully. So yes, there was significant opposition. Dr. Starzl was against it.*

THOMAS STARZL: *I actually thought that [ISMETT] was a mistake.*

JEFFREY A. ROMOFF: *Starzl and I went through a period when he convinced himself that our Italian venture was penurious, profit-seeking, and self-serving. He was entirely against it. And he was against me for a time as well. It was painful for our relationship.*

But, Romoff appends, "I can't remember anything interesting UPMC ever decided to do that didn't have a lot of opposition."

He, Detre, and Michele McKenney, MPH, president of UPMC's Diversified Services, Inc. and UPMC Overseas, traveled to Italy to cultivate relationships with government officials, the Pope, powerful community leaders and esteemed families, and physicians and hospital directors. Detre turned his legendary charm on prominent physicians at the University of Palermo. He presented himself, he claims, "as a sweet old man who had some pleasant experiences to share, so I could make them feel very comfortable."

Thomas Detre, MD (left), and Michele McKenney, MPH (right), oversaw the development of the transplant center at ISMETT. Also pictured (center) is Michael Costelloe, director general of ISMETT from 1998–2005.

Romoff carved out time to learn to speak Italian – and found to his surprise that he was "strangely more comfortable expressing my more emotive personality in Italian than I am in English. I'm actually very proud of learning Italian," he says. "It makes the argument that I care about you and your culture with every sentence I say." He also found himself getting up at two o'clock in the morning in Pittsburgh to talk to people in Italy, reading Italian newspapers, immersing himself in Italian politics, and studying some of Italy's ninety thousand laws. "We did not *impose* ourselves on Italy," Romoff emphasizes. "We didn't go in there and say we're the only ones who know how to do this. We understood what Italy brought to the party; we recruited Italian professionals; we cross-trained them and us together to get this done."

While Detre laid the groundwork at the University of Palermo, Romoff oversaw contract negotiations between UPMC and the Sicilian government. UPMC proposed to manage ISMETT "in a manner which is consistent with the premier [transplant] program in the world."

Beyond the complexities of transplanting "the most sophisticated clinical care that there is," every step of these negotiations was new to both UPMC and the Sicilians. Never before had a public-private partnership been created in this ancient island. Never before had two Palermo hospitals, public Civico and university-related Cervello, agreed to cooperate on a new medical program. Never before had UPMC established a permanent facility in a foreign country, replanting its technology, resources, expertise, and "culture of hunger" in new and potentially barren soil.

But by July 1996 the local and national governments appeared to agree on a letter of intent. Detre and Romoff flew to Italy for the ceremonial signing. In the midst of the negotiations, however, the national government had changed: Prime Minister Silvio Berlusconi of the center-right coalition lost a general election to the center-left's Romano Prodi, threatening to end the entire project before it started.

"This is where I started to get worried," remembers McKenney, who had worked with UPMC leaders since 1985, when she was a young administrator at the Eye & Ear Hospital and the Detre team took over its management. "It became clear to me that the Sicilians had not read the letter of intent we had negotiated. They did not believe it was really going to happen. They knew, in their heart of hearts, that this would never be pulled off."

Officials of the new government began demanding significant changes to the proposed letter of intent. But the new health minister, Rosy Bindi, seemed to know nothing of these demands. After a hastily arranged meeting with Romoff in a private room at the Rome airport, she decided to fly to Sicily for the signing ceremony. On the plane she read both the revised and the original letter of intent – and accepted UPMC's original. She even strengthened UPMC's ability to control staffing for the transplant center. This would be crucial to UPMC's ability to recruit talented people rather than friends of powerful people.

At the televised signing, when Jeffrey A. Romoff gave a graceful speech in Italian, a witness reported that "the expressions on the faces of all the people were of astonishment, admiration and respect." To consider someone *un uomo rispettato* – a respected man who is even a bit feared – is perhaps the highest praise a Sicilian can bestow.

Medically, it seemed, life in Palermo was about to change.

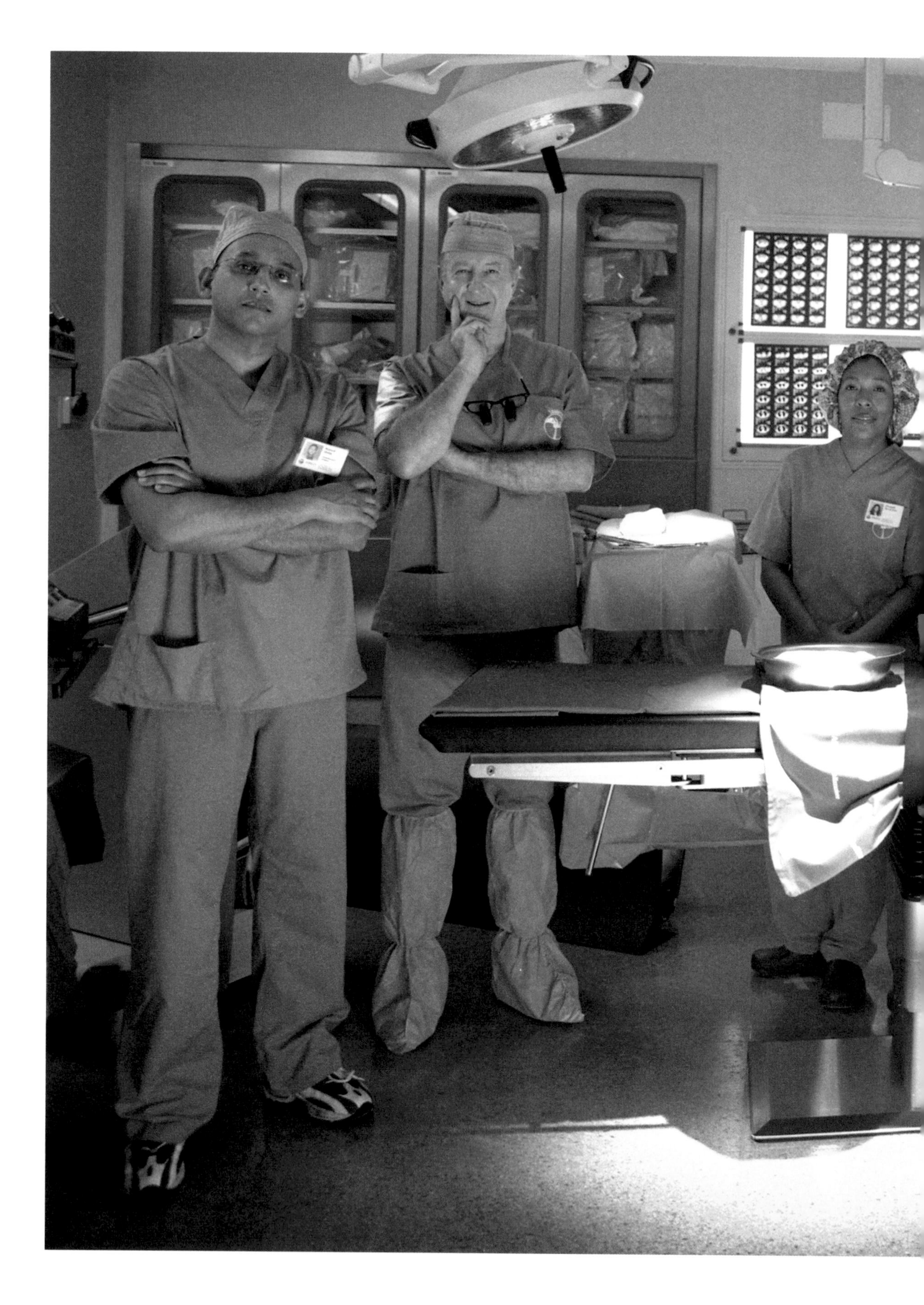

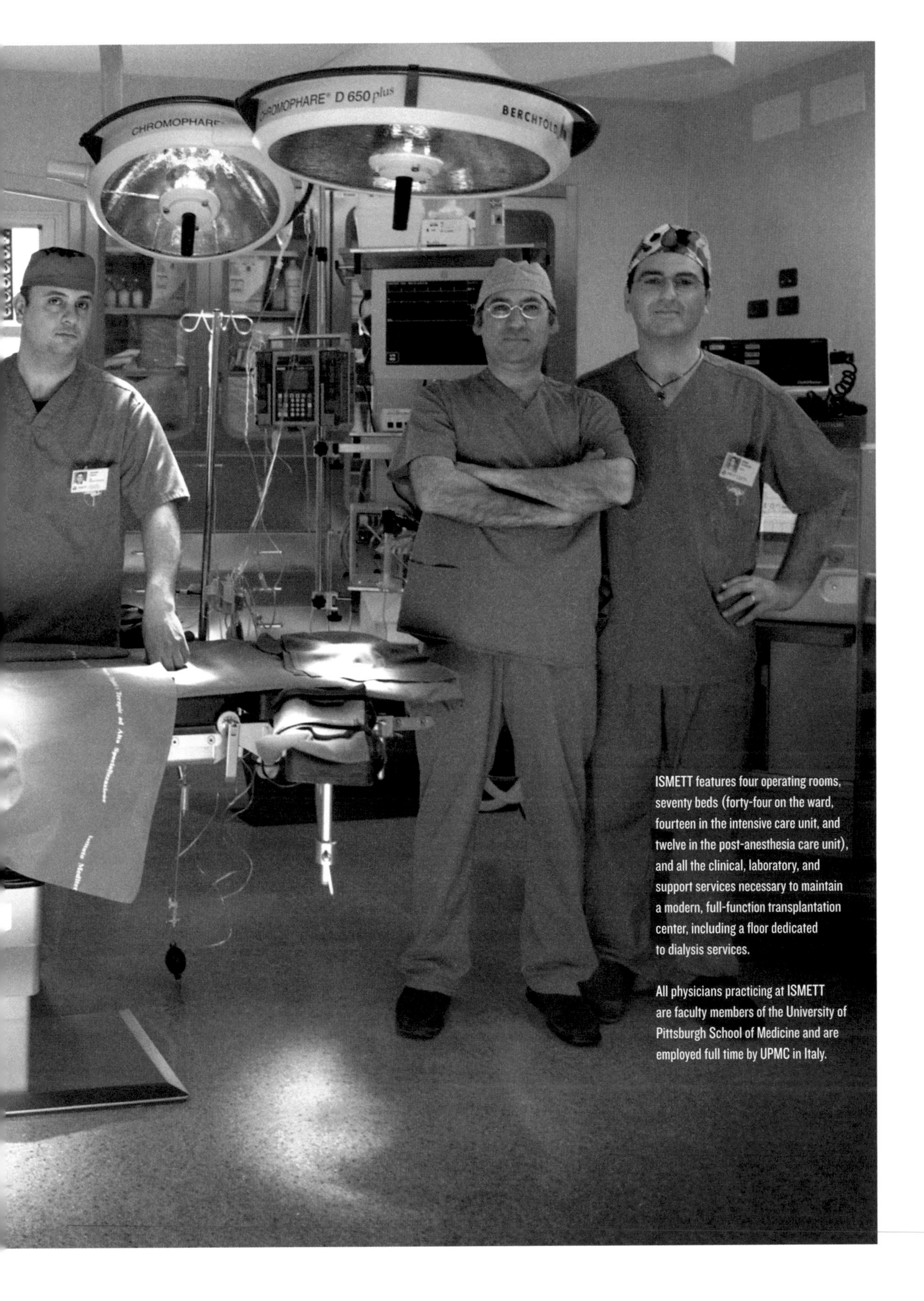

ISMETT features four operating rooms, seventy beds (forty-four on the ward, fourteen in the intensive care unit, and twelve in the post-anesthesia care unit), and all the clinical, laboratory, and support services necessary to maintain a modern, full-function transplantation center, including a floor dedicated to dialysis services.

All physicians practicing at ISMETT are faculty members of the University of Pittsburgh School of Medicine and are employed full time by UPMC in Italy.

Challenges in Palermo

UPMC began working to open a temporary, twenty-bed transplant unit in a newly renovated and equipped wing of Palermo's aging Civico Hospital.

"The day I walked into the space in the hospital where we were going to renovate, I saw heroin needles on the internal steps," says McKenney, who managed the renovation as well as the construction of the new hospital. "But we were able to get it cleaned up. We were able to make two floors of Civico Hospital look as close to an American hospital as we could. The operating rooms became state-of-the-art. And we had wonderful staff there who worked day in and day out to get it done."

There were intricate clinical services and administrative procedures to develop, many of which were the intellectual property of UPMC. There were personnel to recruit, physicians and nurses to train, and proprietary software to customize. There was an organ procurement program to create, and a scientific advisory board and board of directors to establish. Every step had the potential to become "an enterprise of heroic proportions."

Not surprisingly, physicians at the University of Palermo who were not part of ISMETT resented its intrusion. Italy at the time had an abundance of unemployed physicians, and doctors grumbled that "the Americans" were getting money they felt was rightfully theirs. They envied ISMETT's amenities, while they struggled to do their work in a tangle of patched-together hospital buildings with crowded corridors and aging equipment. Others felt bitter about the inevitable comparison between themselves and the specialist outsiders. These influential medical professionals took their complaints to the local government, which "wanted to substantially change the management contract which was originally negotiated, and some even wanted to close [ISMETT]," Detre recalls. In his view, they "missed the point that establishing a center of excellence requires considerable sacrifice."

As UPMC's executive vice president for International and Academic Programs and director of International Medical Affairs, Detre "wanted to be sure that we reduced, not eliminated, as much of the university's hostility throughout this project as possible." And as the Greek historian Herodotus wrote nearly 2,500 years ago, "Force has no place where there is need of skill."

THOMAS DETRE: *They tried to undermine us. [But] the university was very supportive of me; I had academic credentials and spoke the language. When they said something hostile, sort of subtly hostile, I purposely misinterpreted it as if it were the kindest comment I had ever heard; and they were totally unaccustomed to that. I had learned in my earlier years that one of the best ways to discourage hostility is to respond as if the comment were perfectly reasonable.*

ISMETT

ISMETT is an international center for specialized medicine serving the people of the Mediterranean region. The new, five-level, 120,000-square-foot facility was dedicated in early 2004.

Dr. Detre and Michele McKenney hosted a dinner for the warring parties, and he told them "how pleased I was about the developing relationship. And then one of my colleagues from the University of Palermo said to me, 'Are you discouraged?'

"'No,' I said. 'Eventually they will join us, provided that we do well, because we are both well-meaning.'

"He said, 'Don't be discouraged. You know how it is. We tried to create a transplant center for the past twenty years, and we never succeeded. So when you came, we didn't want you to succeed either! But once you do, it will be all right.'

"I don't need to kill my enemies," Detre adds. "I just need to coddle them. Or watch them carefully, and let them know that it's perfectly OK to be opposed to something." He recalls that the secretary of health for Sicily, the Assessore alla Sanità, "wouldn't even look at me for about a year and a half." Then one day the enmity melted; the secretary invited Dr. Detre out to share a good dinner.

At ISMETT, UPMC performs lifesaving transplants and other specialized medical procedures.

There were not-so-veiled threats. At a reception, Detre recounts, "a couple of people came up to me, and one said, 'If you proceed with your plans of creating a multiple organ transplant system here, the consequences for you will be severe.'

"I looked him straight in the eye," remembers Detre, who was then seventy-two years old, "and I said, 'You are going to have a great problem.' He looked astonished. I said, 'Your great problem is that I can't die prematurely anymore.' He was speechless!" Detre notes that the incident was brought to the attention of the head of the anti-Mafia taskforce.

Trucks carrying office computers and lights were hijacked. The operating room air conditioning failed. When a contractor lost out on a contract after the company could not produce what was called an anti-Mafia certificate, the firm sued UPMC, but UPMC won. Both Detre and Romoff believe that anyone who thinks that organized crime in some form does not play a role in the economy in any country today is naive. "There is greater balance [in Sicily] than there used to be," Detre says. "But the airport in Palermo is named after two anti-Mafioso judges who were killed when the road blew up beneath them. So it's better than it was, but I wouldn't say it has disappeared."

When critics attacked the cost of the program, UPMC countered with an analysis showing that ISMETT would actually save money for the Sicilian government and would also bring in new revenues and development for Palermo. The estimated annual expenses of $100 million a year (in 1997), including amortized construction costs, would be a little more than half the $180 million the government had been paying to send Sicilian patients far from home for medical care.

"They're lucky they got UPMC so cheap," a former ISMETT surgeon was quoted as saying in 2004.

"When people didn't want you to do something, the standard excuse was, 'We don't do it this way,'" remarks McKenney.

MICHELE MCKENNEY: *It didn't mean they didn't do it this way, it just meant they did not want to get it done. And when it looked like everybody was going along with something, that probably meant that they weren't. But everything was of heroic proportions. Everything was an opera. ISMETT was an opera. It was a story of people dedicated to a dream, and people dedicated to keeping things status quo. Ultimately the two were integrated into something that was greater than anybody believed it really could be.*

ISMETT's first organ transplant was performed in Palermo on July 30, 1999. *The Wall Street Journal* in 2000 described ISMETT as "currently the most ambitious international effort by a U.S. medical center." The new hospital opened in 2004.

And with success, hostility did, as predicted, begin to dissipate. University of Palermo physicians lined up behind the institute and brought "great moral authority," according to Detre. By 2006 more than a hundred transplants would be performed at ISMETT each year, along with specialized medical procedures never offered before in southern Italy. As former mayor Leoluca Orlando told a reporter in 2005, "When you mentioned Palermo in the north of Italy, people thought, 'Oh, well, Palermo. The Mafia.' Now they are thinking organ transplants and the best medicine in the world."

Jeffrey A. Romoff (left) and Ambassador Paolo Pucci di Benisichi (right), general consul, Italian Ministry of Foreign Affairs, and president of Fondazione Ri.MED

The Pittsburgh Paradigm

What UPMC now exports is basically the paradigm Thomas Detre brought to Pittsburgh in 1973. His theory was that a great department or academic medical center could arise only from the synergy of research, teaching, and patient care. Jeffrey A. Romoff and his colleagues added the factor of entrepreneurial management so that the organization was a fully integrated structure.

UPMC's record of success with the Region of Sicily and ISMETT led in 2009 to a partnership with the Ri.MED Foundation and the University of Pittsburgh School of Medicine to build and manage a new Biomedical Research and Biotechnology Center (BRBC). Programs at the center will represent contemporary themes in

UPMC SETTING UP CANCER CENTERS IN IRELAND USING LOCAL VENTURE'S RADIATION SERVICES

By Christopher Snowbeck
Pittsburgh Post-Gazette

The University of Pitt burgh Medical Cent is looking to capita ize on its expertise i radiation oncology throug hospital partnerships fro California to Ireland.

While UPMC is engaged in tw distinct efforts — one invests in a ne U.S. company and another that targe Europe — the business opportunity i both cases involves working with ho pitals that could not otherwise affor expensive new radiation technology f treating cancer patients.

Linear accelerators — the machine that direct radiation at tumors to shrin or dissolve them — can cost more tha $3 million when outfitted with equi ment to generate tumor images ju prior to treatment, said Paul Vivian the chief executive of California-base Alliance Imaging Inc. These costl machines also are capable of deliverin intensity modulated radiation therap (IMRT), a relatively new form of trea ment.

Currently, about 40 percent of a linear accelerators in the country ar capable of delivering IMRT treatment Mr. Viviano said, while only 2 perce of machines include the imaging equip ment.

UPMC is taking a 20 percent stake i a joint venture with Alliance Imagin to create a firm called Alliance Onco ogy. The new company, which alread has opened two cancer centers in Cal fornia and is developing five more i Massachusetts, will work with midsiz community hospitals that lack access t capital as well as the expertise neede for IMRT treatments.

IMRT treatments must be planne

SEE **UPMC,** PAGE E-

Seeing the gree

biomedical research: drug discovery, vaccine development, tissue engineering and regenerative medicine, development of biomedical devices, structural and computational biology, neurosciences, and molecular imaging.

The Palermo-based Ri.MED Foundation was set up in 2006 by decree of the Italian Presidency of the Council of Ministers. Its founding members include the Italian Presidency of the Council of Ministers, the Presidency of the Region of Sicily, the Italian National Research Council, the University of Pittsburgh, and UPMC. In a region of high unemployment and low per-capita income, the biotech enterprise offers the potential to turn southern Italy into a leader in medical research, to generate jobs and spark economic development, and to improve health care around the world.

Beyond Palermo

UPMC has been named one of "America's Best Hospitals" by *U.S. News & World Report* in its annual rankings.

What Palermo proved to Romoff is that "UPMC has a unique ability to export our best clinical and scientific practices to our international partners."

"We don't see boundaries in the world we live in," states Chuck Bogosta. Experienced in developing cancer centers across western Pennsylvania, he took over the management of not only UPMC's International and Commercial Services Division, but also all cancer-related clinical and research activity of the University of Pittsburgh Cancer Institute. Bogosta saw no reason why UPMC could not leverage this technology and export it abroad. "If we can take the most sophisticated cancer care from Pittsburgh to Johnstown, Pennsylvania, we can take that same care to Ireland."

When Bogosta and other UPMC officials met with members of the Irish government in 2004, Mary Harney, the minister for health and children, asked them how long it would take to bring world-class cancer care to Waterford, in southeast Ireland. The community of almost 48,000 people had no facility for radiation therapy; Waterford residents with cancer had to travel to Cork, eighty miles south and west, or to Dublin, a hundred miles north, to receive treatment.

"Probably two years," was the answer.

"How much would it cost?" Ms. Harney inquired.

"In the range of five million dollars."

"She then turned to the finance minister and asked how long it would take and how much it would cost if the Irish government developed such a cancer center," Bogosta recalls. "He said it would probably be eight years and a hundred million euros."

UPMC's first international cancer center was dedicated in October 2006 by Taoiseach (Prime Minister) Bertie Ahern. Whitfield Cancer Centre patients benefit from advanced radiation and imaging technology developed at UPMC; the model allows medical physicists based in Pittsburgh to share information and expertise with radiation specialists at satellite centers as they develop complex, individual treatment plans for each patient.

At left, UPMC's expansion into Ireland attracted media attention in 2006.

UPMC opened its second international cancer treatment facility at Beacon Hospital in Dublin, Ireland, and later announced it would partner with the Beacon Medical Group to operate the entire hospital.

In 2007 UPMC began operating its second international cancer facility, Beacon Hospital Cancer Centre in Dublin's Beacon Hospital – and in 2008 announced an agreement to manage the entire hospital.

And when the oil-rich Persian Gulf country of Qatar, hoping to become a destination for medical tourism, wanted to improve its emergency medicine services, UPMC signed a five-year, $100 million contract in 2006 to help establish that nation's first Level 1 Trauma Center.

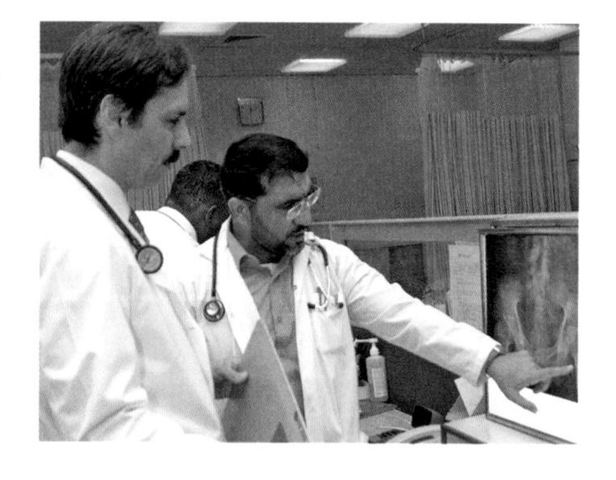

Hamad Medical Corporation is the sole emergency medical service provider in Qatar. The EMS department includes 715 paramedics, dispatchers, call takers, and management staff.

UPMC Needs Challenges

On a wall in Jeffrey A. Romoff's office hangs a map of the world. It reminds him that despite UPMC's achievements in taking its capabilities abroad, "We are once again at the bottom of an even more challenging ladder."

JEFFREY A. ROMOFF: *We are again creating a new technology, learning from our Palermo experience, developing an international export of our services.*

There's this real sense of, my goodness, we have to learn the rules of the game, develop technologies that we haven't developed, we've got to learn to take from here and bring to there, we've got to develop means of transportation, means of communication, et cetera, et cetera – and these are enormous challenges, which brings me back to where we started, which is, this departure, this international programming, is of enormous significance.

People do not generally see health care as generating new technology. But UPMC created new technology – exporting health care to a new place. Once you learn how to export technology, you are in a position to generate new ideas, new businesses, new growth.

And, Romoff repeats, "I think the temperament of this organization, what drives the organization, is it needs challenges."

"We could not have done what we did without regenerating ourselves time and time again. That's the only way to do it. Because the day you stop growing and regenerating is the day you die."

— Jeffrey A. Romoff

Forging a health enterprise for the twenty-first century

2002–2007

2002 G. Nicholas Beckwith III becomes chairperson of the UPMC Board of Directors.

2003–2004 Jeffrey A. Romoff introduces a "new vision" for UPMC's further growth and development.

2005 UPMC creates Strategic Business Initiatives (SBI) to leverage capabilities to generate new revenue streams, commercialize technologies developed in western Pennsylvania, and develop new businesses for the region.

UPMC and IBM announce an unprecedented, eight-year, $402 million agreement to jointly develop software and systems for health care organizations.

2006 UPMC becomes America's first and only nonprofit health enterprise to fully adopt and receive auditor's certification for Sarbanes-Oxley implementation, as well as industry-leading public financial disclosure practices for both quarterly and annual results, allowing community stakeholders to review its progress and fiscal health.

2007 UPMC creates International and Commercial Services Division (ICSD).

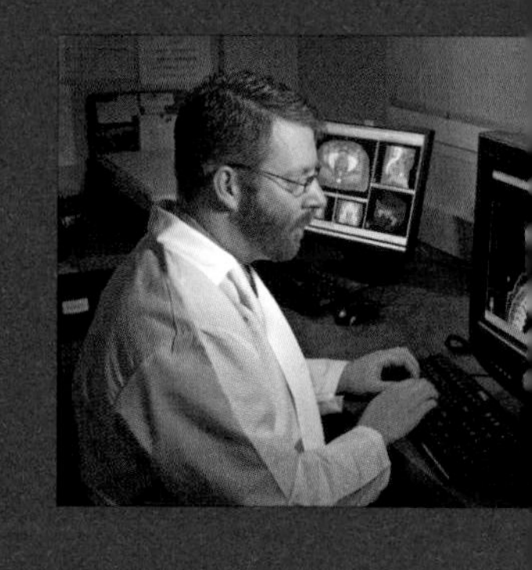

9

UPMC in a New Key

"My job in this place is writing the song, writing the story of UPMC. And I'm always going back and trying to listen to what we wrote and what happened here, and then I'm trying to create, based on that, the next variation on the theme, the next place we can go, the next departure." — Jeffrey A. Romoff

Jeffrey A. Romoff's powerful persona may have antagonized people over the years, but he acknowledges just one formidable antagonist: "the tyranny of dominant paradigms." As the leader of an organization that has changed relentlessly to survive in changing and often hostile environments, Romoff asserts, "We could not have done what we did without regenerating ourselves time and time again. That's the only way to do it. Because the day you stop growing and regenerating is the day you die. And I can't imagine anyone actually signing up to die."

The value Romoff believes he brings and has brought to UPMC is "basically making music – putting together very talented people and resources, helping them harmonize." And, he emphasizes, "Putting pieces together is a high-risk proposition. You have to break the bonds [of a] world you either created or lived in forever." Insularity, though, is "ultimately fatal."

Change for Survival

UPMC entered the twenty-first century as an organization very much *of* the twenty-first century – a knowledge-based, innovative, and flexible service provider, one of the largest integrated health delivery and financing systems in the country. But now a new set of challenges confronted the organization externally and internally. Reimbursement for health care continued to decline, while the population of UPMC's western Pennsylvania home was, at best, stagnant. Striving to rebound from its loss of identity as a steel center, the area struggled to revitalize its economy and create new jobs for the graduates of Pittsburgh's prestigious universities. With the terrorist attacks of September 11, 2001, national military spending mounted, while medical research funding from the National Institutes of Health – funding that had supported so much health care innovation throughout the United States – declined in actual dollars and, more importantly, in purchasing power.

Established academic medical centers can rely on their endowments when times get tough, but scrappy young UPMC did not have that luxury. What Romoff felt he had to do in the early 2000s was shake up the huge organization he had spent half of his life helping to create. He had to analyze the potential value of the abundant, sprawling resources of people and technology that UPMC had amassed, and then develop strategies to exploit these resources. And with the retirement of Dr. Thomas Detre from the university and from day-to-day participation in UPMC activities, as well as the 2003 decision of longtime Executive Vice President John Paul to make a sabbatical permanent, Romoff now had to reshape the UPMC management team. "Everybody thought we were vulnerable when John left," Romoff admits.

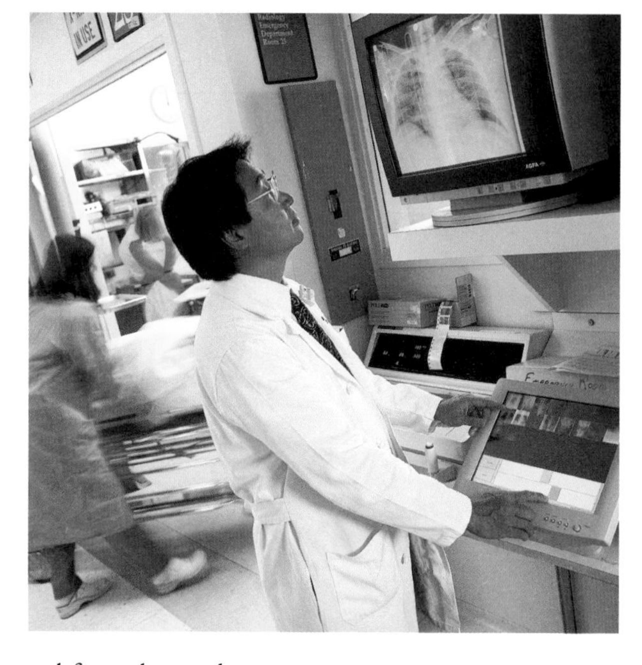

UPMC delivers CT scans and other diagnostic images on demand.

At that point the one-time bandleader says that, for the first time, he recognized the true value of leadership to an organization. He began to appreciate "how a conductor can actually take great players and come up with something that exceeds their capacity, because the whole is greater than the sum of the individual parts."

In 2003 and 2004 Romoff risked jarring UPMC's harmony by introducing a new key: adding on a new business dimension in hopes of making the future even stronger. He defines his new vision as "completely beyond the pale of anyone that calls themselves an academic medical center in the world today."

A New Business Model

In order to continue to grow, evolve, improve, direct money toward the core academic mission, and help jump-start the economy in western Pennsylvania, Romoff decided that UPMC would build from the platform of its integrated health and financing system a new business model: a global health enterprise.

At the Center for Connected Medicine, UPMC, IBM, Alcatel-Lucent, Cerner, and other industry partners showcase integrated technology solutions in practice at UPMC which reduce costs and improve patient care.

His response to adverse local and national economic conditions was characteristically iconoclastic: UPMC would go beyond the bounds of traditional health care. If health care was in a war to survive cuts in reimbursement and to create new efficiencies, he saw no reason why UPMC could not collaborate with major technology vendors on "mini-Manhattan projects" to generate new products and new sources of revenue. At a time when conventional wisdom focused on sickness in the health care system, he recognized that UPMC people had already crafted some very healthy technical and operational prescriptions.

JEFFREY A. ROMOFF: *In the U.S. we have some of the finest health care in the world, delivered in the most dysfunctional and expensive ways imaginable. In contrast to this disorganization, UPMC is built on marrying the disparate parts of health care. The UPMC model is a highly integrated delivery system that provides every aspect of care; that utilizes information technology to get the right information to the right place at the right time; that educates the next generation of health care professionals; that blends the strengths of academic and private-practice physicians; that quickly translates research from bench to bedside – and does all these things as part of the same system.*

This expertise had quantifiable value, Romoff believed. He pushed UPMC to compete in what *The New York Times* columnist and author Thomas L. Friedman calls a "flattened" world – a world where barriers between disciplines, institutions, and nations are dissolving. He urged UPMC to create commercialization ventures and new businesses; to develop and sell products or services; to export UPMC's intellectual capital, managerial models, and clinical capabilities; and to launch unprecedented strategic partnerships with multinational corporations.

How do you prepare an organization to make this kind of change? Romoff likens the approach to creating music.

JEFFREY A. ROMOFF: *First of all, you have to listen. If you are going to write an orchestration, although you can't necessarily play a trumpet and a clarinet and a viola and a bass fiddle, you have to know enough about their range, enough about their capacity.*

Then you've got to convince the players to leave their solo worlds and collaborate and combine with many other pieces, which may or may not mean a diminution of certain things that they do – it may mean only playing for ten bars instead of for ten minutes – for the greater good of the orchestration.

In creating this new model, Romoff recognizes, "This is not an issue [merely] of grafting on to what you already have. You remake everything. Everything is up for grabs. It's a whole new mix. So it becomes an extraordinarily creative challenge."

G. Nicholas Beckwith III became chair of the UPMC Board of Directors in 2002.

Successful Organizations Do Not Stand Still

Romoff's ideas for revenue development had the support of UPMC's new board chair, G. Nicholas Beckwith III, a business and community leader with almost thirty years' experience as a hospital trustee. A disciplined thinker and outstanding communicator, he, too, was comfortable with change. Like Romoff, he understood that successful organizations cannot and do not stand still.

And as a native Pittsburgher with a keen commitment to western Pennsylvania, Beckwith also understood UPMC's powerful impact on the region's economy and quality of life. He felt that UPMC, as the region's largest employer, should be an active community citizen.

In particular, Beckwith pushed the organization to become a national leader in quality and patient safety, as well as a model of corporate transparency. "Ongoing improvement in the attainment of better outcomes in all varieties of all the benchmarks is to me the real litmus test of success," he has said. "And clearly, you don't get sustained quality without a strong financial base."

At WPIC, Jeffrey A. Romoff had readily taken on the establishment to introduce new models of administration, reimbursement, and delivery of mental health services. Thirty years later he again fought the dominant paradigm, which this time insisted that there were no examples of success stories for health care systems that could both provide superb patient care and at the same time commercialize their capabilities on a large scale across multiple domains.

"Pittsburgh," Theodore Roosevelt said in 1917, "has not been built up by talking about it. Your tremendous institutions were built by [people] who actually *did the work.*" Romoff says the same about his colleagues.

JEFFREY A. ROMOFF: *Other organizations ... think because they have a vision ... that they can actually do it. Getting it done is really very hard. And we have a very good team of people to get it done, who are self-motivated, driven, very effective, and we constantly replenish that team with new ideas and new people to get things done.*

"At UPMC you're never satisfied," asserts Dan Drawbaugh, UPMC's longtime chief information officer.

DAN DRAWBAUGH: *You can do something that somebody feels is great today, and tomorrow you're like, "I haven't done anything in twenty-four hours. I've got to go do something creative, innovative." The environment, the culture that permeates UPMC is innovation and being creative and being aggressive. You're allowed to do that; you're encouraged to do that. It's a driven organization, and if you're driven as an individual, you want to be part of a driven organization.*

"To Jeff's credit very much, he allowed the managers to do what they do," said the late UPMC director Donald D. Wolff Jr. "And these are extraordinarily bright, hard-working, effective people, people who are capable in many aspects of the organization. It was an empowering organizational change."

UPMC's management culture impressed Robert DeMichiei when he worked for GE Energy. "What attracted me to UPMC is the same caliber of executive talent I would see at GE – results-measured, successful, passionate," he comments. A Pittsburgh-area native, DeMichiei returned home in 2004 to be UPMC's chief financial officer.

Robert A. DeMichiei, senior vice president, UPMC and chief financial officer, found the same "results-measured, successful, passionate culture" at UPMC as he had known at GE Energy — and "GE is known to have a great management team."

"This place runs 24/7," says Chuck Bogosta. "We get decisions – decisions that are handled by multiple committees in other organizations – at three o'clock in the morning! And we probably wrote the e-mail at eleven o'clock that night. That defines everything as far as I'm concerned."

Elizabeth B. Concordia contrasts UPMC with other academic medical centers that are "typically risk-averse, slow to make decisions, and very deeply mired in politics. [But] the entrepreneurial pace at which things occur here is absolutely different from other academic medical centers. And I think that's one of the many reasons that UPMC is so successful today, without a doubt."

Information Technology as a Platform

Between 2001 and 2005, UPMC invested well over $500 million in information technology (IT); by 2007 this investment would top $1 billion. In 2006 CIO Dan Drawbaugh was named Chief Information Officer of the Year by *InformationWeek* magazine for his aggressive development and unparalleled use of IT to transform health care. Health care is "the most information-intensive industry in the world," according to Scott Lammie, chief financial officer, UPMC Health Plan. "It's also very critical because you're making minute-to-minute, life-or-death decisions. So we continue to work on pulling all that information into a comprehensive, integrated package."

IT is the backbone of UPMC's clinical operations, according to G. Daniel Martich, MD, the physician who heads UPMC's electronic health record system, eRecord. Beyond eRecord, UPMC also relies on information technology to benchmark and measure performance. "If you really want to know what goes on in an operation, you actually have to automate it," believes Elizabeth Concordia. "It's all in the detail."

A big part of UPMC's success rests on what Drawbaugh calls "specialized, advanced, clinical decision-support tools to deliver the best possible care and to ensure that you're delivering it every single time in the same way."

Dan Drawbaugh, senior vice president, UPMC and chief information officer, was named "CIO of the Year" by *InformationWeek* magazine in 2006.

At UPMC, leading experts in neurosurgery, otolaryngology and ophthalmology collaborate to provide innovative treatments for hard-to-reach brain tumors.

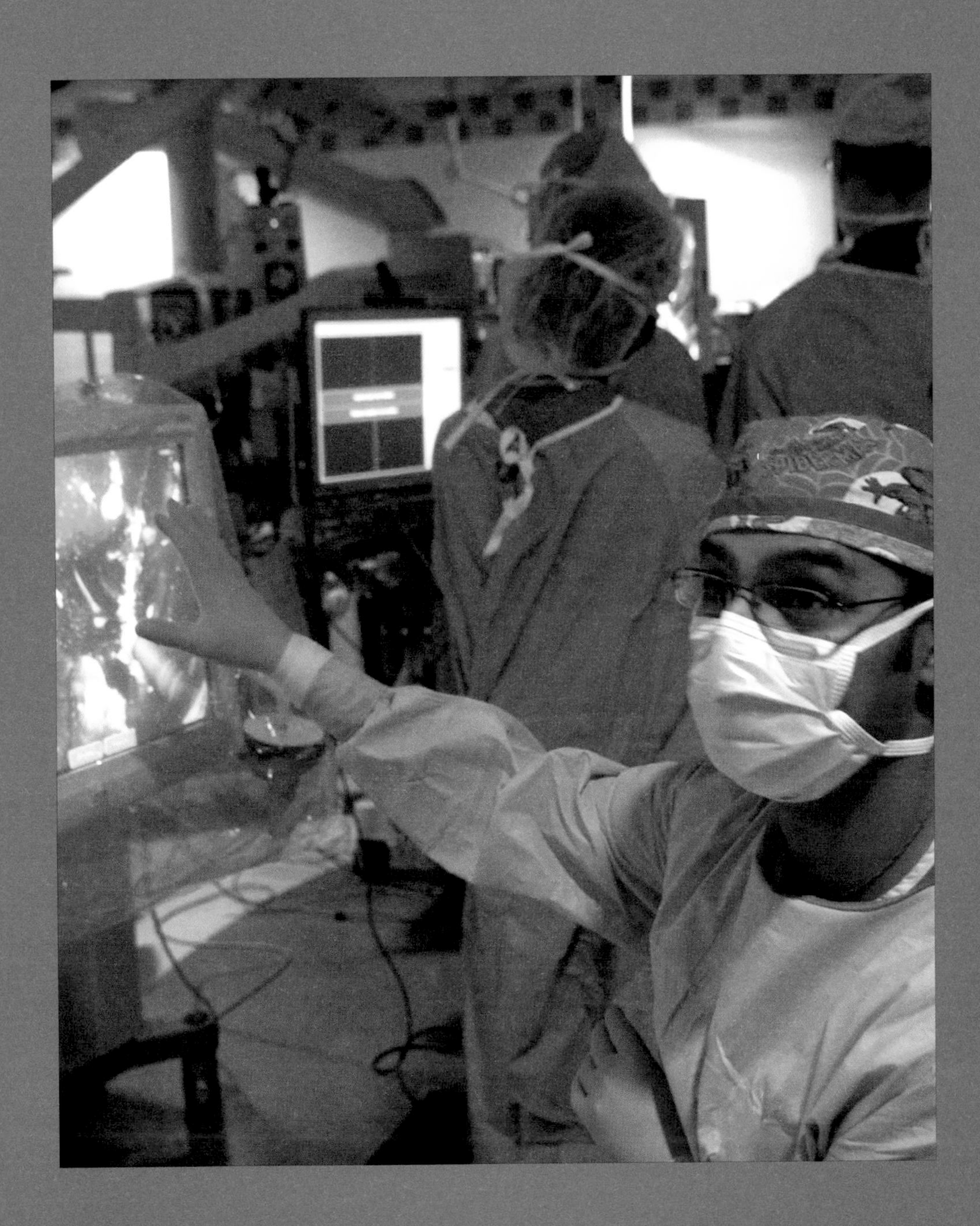

At a press conference on April 28, 2005, Jeffrey A. Romoff (left) and Dan Pelino, IBM general manager, Global Healthcare and Life Sciences Industry (right), announced an eight-year, $402 million agreement to codevelop technology solutions to two of the most pressing issues facing health care: quality and costs.

"An Eye-Opening Megadeal"

Where once WPIC had developed collaborations with university departments and state psychiatric hospitals, now UPMC forged major strategic partnerships with multinational corporations such as General Electric and Cerner. These precedent-setting partnerships leveraged UPMC's leadership in health-domain information technology and biotechnology. For developers and sellers of technology, UPMC offered the advantage of being able to prove the efficacy of their product quickly.

The strategy transformed UPMC's relationships with its major vendors. "We not only look at buying a product from a vendor, but we select [vendors] as strategic partners," says Drawbaugh. "I'm looking for someone that has the same desire and drive to develop the unique, next-generation solution together."

SANDRA DANOFF: *These organizations, which are many-fold larger than we are, have found that we have a set of operational capabilities that very nicely complements their technological capabilities. So these are true strategic partnerships, with both sides being able to bring something to the table that the other side desperately needed.*

A bold new partnership was announced in April 2005: an eight-year, $402 million joint development agreement with IBM, the largest IT corporation in the world. The unprecedented pact involved a commitment from both IBM and UPMC to invest at least $25 million each toward the joint development of software and systems for health care organizations – "the infrastructure of the future." The goal is to enhance patient safety and make health care more efficient by integrating digitized information seamlessly.

Romoff defined the IBM–UPMC joint venture capital fund as "the heart of inventing the future of health care. The implications in biosecurity, in cost control, and in quality management are just enormous."

Modern Healthcare magazine saw it as "a landmark agreement that will blaze an IT path for the rest of the industry, which has been struggling to seamlessly automate the clinical and administrative sides of its businesses." *InformationWeek* magazine went further, describing the accord as an "eye-opening megadeal."

Bringing New Concepts and Emerging Technologies to Market

UPMC, its managers say, learns from its mistakes as well as its triumphs. Stentor, a company that provides technology for storing, managing, and distributing digital radiology images, offered a lesson in both. "Stentor we describe as our best and our worst example of a commercial activity," comments Chuck Bogosta.

Stentor was a technology that was developed at UPMC. UPMC was the primary reference site; UPMC deployed it throughout its entire system; and UPMC demonstrated the return on investment. Then, says Philip Green, former president of UPMC's Strategic Business Initiatives unit, "We went to the venture capital community, which put up $10 or $15 million to commercialize it. Then the company was sold in 2005 to Philips for about $280 million. UPMC and the University of Pittsburgh together got about $40 or $50 million of that amount." What UPMC learned is that the venture capitalists made a big return on their investment, and they added what UPMC saw as relatively little value.

CHARLES BOGOSTA: *So what we learned on that is when we have a great idea, we should not be giving the equity away to a partner who's just a money partner. The lesson is, if we were going to continue to do things like Stentor and related commercial opportunities, why not put up our money instead of getting venture money – and keep the proceeds of the business we generated?*

When UPMC launched the new unit Strategic Business Initiatives (SBI), it set about becoming a hands-on equity partner in commercial opportunities. "SBI was a creation of UPMC to use the platform we created in western Pennsylvania to commercialize ideas outside western Pennsylvania," sums up Philip Green. He believes that this going-at-risk strategy "is totally, totally unique."

PHILIP GREEN: *Nobody has ever done it. Nobody else is doing it today. The difference is, there are a lot of academic medical centers who generate research and related initiatives and license their technologies to multinational companies. That's the traditional academic center model. But they don't actually invest their own funds in order to generate the business, and they also don't take part in actively developing and marketing the business on their own, which is what we do. There's nobody who has the model like this.*

Because of the promise of its early efforts in commercializing and exporting its core capabilities, UPMC in 2007 formed the International and Commercial Services Division (ICSD) to operate and manage these commercial opportunities.

Jeffrey A. Romoff had proposed that UPMC "use our resources to effect the transformation of health care technology." According to Robert Cindrich, UPMC's chief legal officer, "We've now got universities calling us and saying, 'Couldn't you come down and show us how you ... harness the clinical part of the practice in such a way that it will support the medical school?'"

ROBERT CINDRICH: *What I tell them is this: IBM doesn't give away its technology, and neither does Mr. Gates. Our technology today, broadly defined, is the ability to manage an academic medical center, which means to provide for its information technology needs, its revenue cycle needs, its supply chain needs, its administration of hospital and patient care needs. It is intellectual property. We own it. It may not be a specific thing, but the collective bundle of information and skills that we can put together has great value.*

Now, if another entity wants to have us apply that technology to their situation, we want to be paid for it. Why? So we can take that money back here to Pittsburgh and reinvest it in health care services, jobs ... things that benefit this community.

What are the predictions for the future of technology export?

CHARLES BOGOSTA: *We spend every single day talking about that. We're trying to figure out what our place is in the market, what we should be like, and how we should focus our energy. What we've concluded, though, is that we should be taking a longer-term view. To do it right, you need to take a three- to five-year view as opposed to a twelve-month view, which is what you do in the traditional world of health care. And so it takes a different kind of mind-set.*

The Hon. Robert J. Cindrich stepped down as a judge of the United States District Court for Western Pennsylvania to become senior vice president and chief legal officer, UPMC.

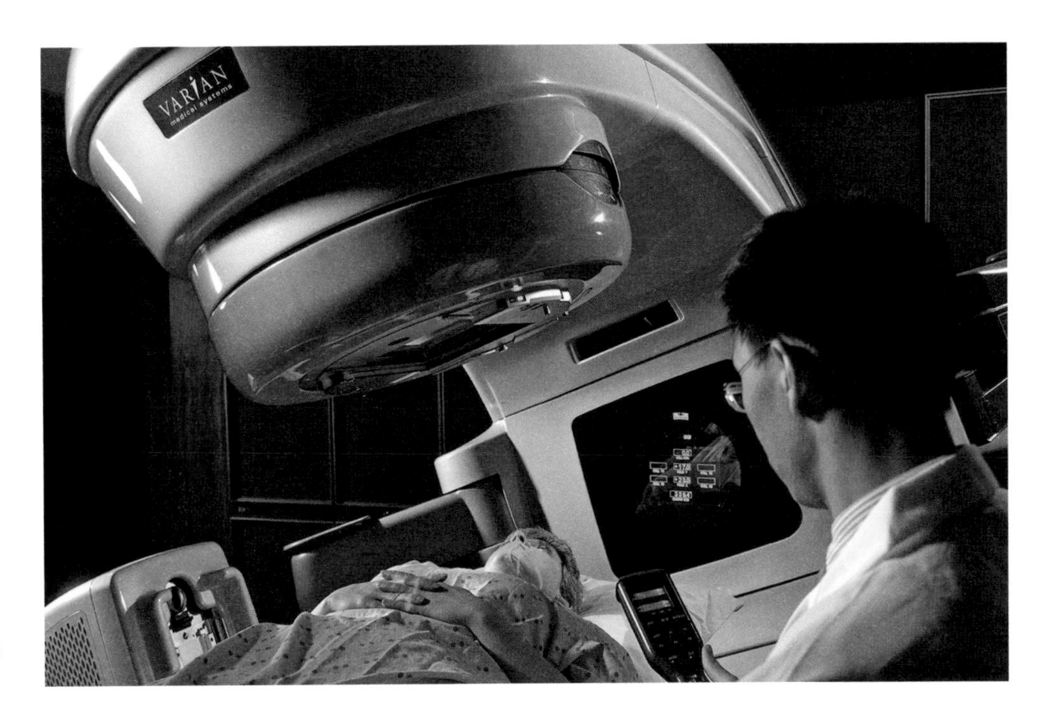

UPMC offers remote radiation treatment planning to enable patients across the globe to receive world-class cancer care.

ROBERT CINDRICH: *My sense is that we've only just begun to figure out ways to mine our intellectual capital and our know-how, and make that into businesses and to make those businesses create jobs.*

Romoff has never shied away from the challenge of transforming the organization he leads. "There's always a storyline," he muses, "and the storyline comes up continuously against new reality. And we have to change the story."

JEFFREY A. ROMOFF: *And I'm willing to change the story, because unlike most authors I'm not entirely invested in the story that worked for me for six months. In fact, the longer the story works for me, the more I get a real sense of uneasiness that I've become rigid and stupid and bound into my own fantasy life, and I'm missing these cues. Because you can't help but notice that the world changes, life changes, the people around me change, I change, everything changes. And if I'm not modifying the story …*

"UPMC is always changing. That's what makes it exciting. When an organization advances the way UPMC has, it's because there's a pace and an expectation of change."

— Elizabeth B. Concordia

2007–2009

Mining intellectual capital, investing in the community, and setting the stage for a new export economy

2007 UPMC announces a $100 million commitment to The Pittsburgh Promise, a fund that will help students graduating from the Pittsburgh Public Schools to further their education after high school.

2008 To help revitalize downtown Pittsburgh and to create a corridor for an economic renaissance stretching from Oakland to downtown, UPMC moves its headquarters to the U. S. Steel Tower.

2009 Just as nineteenth-century industry transformed Pittsburgh and re-engineered industrial processes, UPMC has created — and continues to create — new models of health care delivery, management, and financing today.

Pittsburgh Mayor Bob O'Connor (right), whose enthusiasm for his city was unbounded, signed one of the final steel beams for the new Children's Hospital of Pittsburgh of UPMC in 2006, just a few months before he died.

10

Look Back ... and Imagine the Future

"We didn't build UPMC because we were building a model. We did it because it was the right thing to do." — Jeffrey A. Romoff

A snapshot of UPMC in 2008 reveals the leading integrated health system in Pennsylvania and one of the largest and most diverse in the United States, a system with $7.8 billion in assets, $7.1 billion in operating revenues, and 50,000 employees – and a more than fifty-fold increase in revenue between 1988 and 2008. If UPMC were a Fortune 500 company, it would rank around 350th in revenue.

Over the past generation, the development of UPMC may be the biggest, most interesting, and perhaps least understood story of Pittsburgh and western Pennsylvania. Just as nineteenth-century Pittsburghers transformed Pittsburgh and re-engineered industrial processes in their time, Thomas Detre, Jeffrey A. Romoff, and their colleagues have created – and continue to create – new models of health care delivery, management, and financing in theirs.

When Detre and Romoff came to Pittsburgh, manufacturing accounted for 24.2 percent of Pittsburgh-area employment, and health care 6.5 percent. By 2008 manufacturing provided 8.6 percent of the jobs, and health care, with 15.5 percent of the workforce, was the region's dominant employer. Only Boston, with 16.5 percent, had a higher percentage of medical positions.

And like the great, historic rivers that flow through and beyond Pittsburgh, at UPMC there is always a sense of motion. Motion, change, adaptation, evolution. "History ... is always seen through today's eyes, because today's eyes change [the way we see the past]," Romoff believes. He can distill the history of UPMC to "just a simple story of coming of age ... against enormous resistance."

JEFFREY A. ROMOFF: *I cannot imagine life without that process of coming of age. And I cannot imagine institutional growth and survival without a constant process of renewal and re-creation. We are all so in need of some growth, creating for tomorrow something better than what we have today ... that it is a natural act.*

Romoff also insists that "everything to me has to have a coherence." Perhaps UPMC's coherence, its gravitational pull, is evolution itself.

JEFFREY A. ROMOFF: *What all of us accomplished, particularly over the last ten years, of making an integrated delivery system, is unique, and the more places I go, the more I appreciate it. [But] every time I get to a top of a mountain, I see another mountain higher. Thereby I have a sense of being at the bottom of the mountain range.*

GEORGE HUBER: *Dr. Detre was always driving, always driving. And Jeff Romoff's the same way. All he says is we are going to continuously grow. He's a grower, not a maintainer. Jeff could have sat back and said, "Man, we've got the finest medical center here; I'm happy; we're going to ride this out and just leave it where it's at." No. No way. He says, "We should start leveraging what we're doing. Because if we do that, we'll garner revenues and those revenues can be used to enhance the academic mission."*

And it has worked.

"UPMC is hungry; it's not afraid to act; it's a decisive organization; and it's going to continue to grow. And I think we'll have more and more of an impact on changing the landscape in health care."

— ELIZABETH B. CONCORDIA

CHILDREN'S HOSPITAL OF PITTSBURGH OF UPMC

Renowned for outstanding clinical services, research programs, and medical education, Children's Hospital of Pittsburgh of UPMC is one of the top-ranking pediatric hospitals in the United States. The new hospital, set on a ten-acre campus in Pittsburgh's Lawrenceville neighborhood, includes a 1.5-million-square-foot hospital and a ten-story research center.

Doing It Right

If UPMC coheres around risk and reinvention, it also revolves around a continuing commitment to excellence in academic medicine and clinical care. UPMC has made western Pennsylvania a far healthier and more vibrant place in which to live and work. "I always had to believe that what we were doing was for the good of man, doing the 'right thing,'" Romoff asserts. "And if an organization is to be effective, it needs to have a sense of inner integrity."

JEFFREY A. ROMOFF: *The reason UPMC is successful is because we are just absolutely committed to doing things well. UPMC had the privilege of doing what was right most of the time. In fact, almost all the time. We made mistakes, in hindsight. But not many.*

UPMC pays tens of millions of dollars in taxes and voluntary contributions annually. UPMC contributes more than half a billion dollars annually to the region and its residents in uncompensated care for those unable to pay, covering shortfalls in government programs for low-income households; support for research and education; and federal taxes that secure the future for UPMC's western Pennsylvania employees. Yet the organization is frequently criticized for being too successful. The implication seems to be that health systems should be meek and unbusinesslike – the way hospitals used to be seventy-five years ago.

ROBERT DEMICHIEI: *It's as if we are penalized for our efficiency. By doing the right thing we get more enemies. But not-for-profit does not mean no-profit. Without profits, we would not be able to reinvest in our community.*

Magee-Womens Hospital of UPMC President Leslie C. Davis, who is also vice president of Women and Infants Health Services, UPMC, came to Pittsburgh in 2004 from Philadelphia, where four medical schools compete. "Here in Pittsburgh," she says, "there's a lot more focus on patient care, which is where it should be, and not on the CEO of the other hospital."

LESLIE DAVIS: *At UPMC we spend a lot more time focusing on quality initiatives and figuring out how to create a better patient experience. The spend on capital is enormous. To put this in perspective, my first year here, I think our capital spend for information technology at UPMC exceeded the capital budgets for [Philadelphia's] Penn and Jefferson hospitals combined, the entire capital budgets. So when you think about our ability to do new things, the potential is enormous.*

Esther L. Bush (left), president of the Urban League of Greater Pittsburgh, chairs the Diversity Committee of UPMC's Board of Directors.

"I'm very proud to say that UPMC is a leader in the community – I put them as number one now," comments Esther L. Bush, the UPMC director who is president of the Urban League of Greater Pittsburgh. "I am so proud that whenever you see a special event, whenever you see a community activity, whenever you see anything big or small, UPMC is one of the sponsors."

In what is believed to be the largest commitment of its kind, UPMC announced in December 2007 that it would contribute $100 million to a program that will help students graduating from the Pittsburgh Public Schools to further their education after high school. UPMC offered an initial $10 million to mobilize The Pittsburgh Promise in time to support 2008 Pittsburgh Public School graduates. The remaining $90 million came in the form of a challenge grant. UPMC hopes it will spur a communitywide campaign to raise a total of $250 million for a permanent endowment to fund future generations of graduates.

Pittsburgh Public Schools Superintendent Mark Roosevelt and others believe The Pittsburgh Promise will make the city and its public schools more attractive to families and their children and will raise expectations and academic performance. "What you really have to do to make your life be all that it can be is to dream big and work hard," Roosevelt said. "As the leading employer and economic engine of our region, UPMC exemplifies this."

Pittsburgh Mayor Luke Ravenstahl (below, left) and Pittsburgh Public Schools Superintendent Mark Roosevelt (right) joined UPMC President Jeffrey A. Romoff to announce UPMC's $10 million lead gift and a future commitment of up to $90 million in matching funds for The Pittsburgh Promise. This incentive will help students graduating from Pittsburgh Public Schools to further their education after high school.

In 2008 UPMC moved its headquarters to and placed its name atop downtown Pittsburgh's tallest building, a move which contributed to revitalizing the city's central business district.

U. S. STEEL TOWER

Clyde B. Jones III, president, Medical and Health Sciences Foundation and chief development officer, UPMC

"Dr. Thomas Detre and his successor, Jeffrey A. Romoff, smashed a lot of cherished 'eggs' on the way to creating the present awesome 'omelet.' Suffice it to say, the entrepreneurial Dr. Detre, with his phenomenal ability to attract federal grants, will be seen in the history books as one of the makers of modern Pittsburgh."

— Clarke Thomas, late senior editor, *Pittsburgh Post-Gazette*

Clyde B. Jones III, president, Medical and Health Sciences Foundation and chief development officer, UPMC, has a significant interest in the arts and supports UPMC's increasing interaction with the region.

CLYDE JONES: *Mr. Romoff and I have had lots of conversations about the reasons that people come to Pittsburgh and stay here. And we know that in Pittsburgh you can enjoy some of the finest arts and cultural offerings of any place in the country. And that will draw people, and that will keep people. So it's a little self-serving because we want our employees and our loved ones to feel happy here and to stay here.*

UPMC demonstrated its commitment to Pittsburgh and western Pennsylvania in April 2008 by moving its corporate headquarters from Oakland to the U. S. Steel Tower, bringing thousands of UPMC employees to the downtown area. Pittsburgh's tallest building now serves as a hub to foster new business development locally and to expand UPMC's national and international initiatives. The move symbolizes, Romoff says, UPMC's goal of "becoming a new export engine for this region."

So What Have We Done?

"So what have we done over the years?" asks Dr. Loren Roth. "If you put it all together, what is the success?"

LOREN ROTH: *There is a great deal of management intelligence. What has happened is a group of very creative, very intelligent people, all with ethical conscience about what is right, [has] made a series of management moves, watching where the money was, watching where the control was, watching where the size was – we made it up, every time, but it is my belief that ... this success has been a clever merging of the academic interests with the clinical interests, which actually are reciprocal and actually help grow a great medical center.*

There's nothing like UPMC. And when you go around the country, their eyes bulge. And you know why? It's not traditional for the health care system to employ the faculty. It's not traditional to have the chairs on an incentive system and to hold them to expectations. These are very unusual things. It's not usual to have [so much money] to invest [in the School of Medicine].

"UPMC as a business institution is fully behind the development of academic programs," declares Dr. Richard L. Simmons, Distinguished Service Professor of Surgery and chair emeritus, Department of Surgery. "That's what's missing in other places."

"To summarize," says Dr. Arthur S. Levine, senior vice chancellor for the Health Sciences and dean of the University of Pittsburgh School of Medicine, "a combination of circumstances, including highly intelligent, aggressive, and creative leadership, great attention to managerial detail, focus on quality, and, at least to an extent, good luck, have eventuated in UPMC's success. In turn, the capacity of UPMC for funds-transfer to the medical school has been a major element in our success as well."

Elizabeth B. Concordia, executive vice president, UPMC and president, Hospital and Community Services Division

MARK NORDENBERG: *When I came to Pittsburgh, this city was known almost exclusively for football, ketchup, and steel – all of which are among my favorite things. But today, when you travel to more distant locations – not just in this country but around the world – the thing that people most often recognize about Pittsburgh is that it is a world center, really, of health care and pioneering research.*

Now UPMC is again mining resources – its own intellectual capital – to help build a great region.

SANDRA DANOFF: *This is the big ambition, this is the vision: to help revitalize the economy in western Pennsylvania, to harness the intellectual capital in a way that creates a new export economy.*

Now, where are we on the slope? It's obvious that we are relatively low on the slope, but I believe this can be done. Pittsburgh has a tradition of building an economy on its natural resources, and today part of those resources reside[s] here at UPMC. Is it going to be possible? Well, UPMC has been reinventing itself and creating the future for the nearly twenty years I've been here. So when people can put aside disbelief, I can say that two years, three years, four years, five years from now, what we'll see in western Pennsylvania is something new, something amazing, something that we will all take pride in.

What I would ask you to do is to look back, and to imagine the future.

Beyond the bounds of Pittsburgh and western Pennsylvania, UPMC's processes and culture may have remedies to help cure a very sick U.S. health care system. "The ability to go from nothing to where we are today … was only accomplished because of the culture that was here," states Elizabeth Concordia.

ELIZABETH CONCORDIA: *UPMC is hungry; it's not afraid to act; it's a decisive organization; and it's going to continue to grow. And I think we'll have more and more of an impact on changing the landscape in health care. The landscape is always changing. But we're setting the stage in simulation. We're setting the stage in a lot of the quality initiatives we're doing. We're setting the stage in transparency. We're setting the stage in the advancement of the academic areas into the clinical side. We are the leaders in all of these – in training and education too.*

Developing a high-quality, cost-effective health system has implications far beyond Pittsburgh. The growth of health care spending in the United States is unsustainable in the long run.

C. TALBOT HEPPENSTALL: *UPMC is actually developing the model that eventually the United States would say, "This is how you do it right, how you manage costs, how you hardwire quality." I'm looking forward to the day when we can say, "The future of health care in the U.S. started right here!"*

"I've never seen a medical system that keeps wanting to grow and push the barriers out and out and out," says Pennsylvania Governor Edward G. Rendell about UPMC.

But while the aspirations are noble, reinvention is rarely a route to popularity. Uprooting comfortable if outworn assumptions and behaviors threatens and scares most people. It makes them suspicious. Driving through the barriers of dominant paradigms "requires a high tolerance for not being liked," as Romoff is the first to say.

EDWARD G. RENDELL: *I think every large organization takes on, to some extent, the personality of whoever the CEO is. If it's an orchestra, they take on the personality of the maestro. If it's a city, it very much takes on the personality of the mayor. So I think that it's natural, to some extent, that UPMC takes on the personality of the president and CEO. Throughout the whole UPMC system, people I've met are imbued with this attitude that (a) there's no hurdle or challenge too big for us, and (b) what can we do to help?*

I have never seen a medical system that is so impactful. And … I've never seen a medical system that keeps wanting to grow and move and push the barriers out and out and out, and expand their horizon and their impact.

And some people say, "This is just a case of the system being empire builders for the sake of building the empire." But I don't believe that's the case. Does Jeff like having new projects? Absolutely. But I think it's not projects for the sake of projects. It's projects because of the belief that those projects will render a great deal of good.

Thomas Detre, MD

Jeffrey A. Romoff

JEFFREY A. ROMOFF: *The adversarial reality of the history of UPMC was confirmatory of everything we were doing. At the time, subjectively, I was angry, and sometimes licking my wounds, and feeling put-upon, and all that. But the overriding sense, when we finally won … was, you know, it was worth the struggle.*

My experience at UPMC, of all these thirty-plus years, is far more joy than there is conflict. For every one of these stories I can tell you, there are a hundred or a thousand stories of collaboration, whether it be with Dr. Detre, my administrative colleagues, of discovery, or of fabulous intellectual stimulation in working with the likes of Starzl, or Simmons, or Fisher, or many of the chairmen.

I mean, the real diet of UPMC, and increasingly so now, is a diet of creation, and this is constant. And even in the midst of all these push-backs, these conflicts, these attempts to get us – they were only rude interruptions to a general story of growth and success and fun.

It's been a very joyous experience. And it still is. I have that same sense of newness, of magic, of discovery, of not having arrived, of being nowhere near having arrived, quite frankly, as I had thirty years ago. And we'll run up against resistances, and we always do as we go along. But that's the sense of UPMC. It's a joyous sense.

NOTES

UPMC gratefully acknowledges the participation of all interviewees.

Most of the quoted material in this history derives from tape-recorded interviews, mostly personal but, as noted below, some by telephone. Mary Brignano and George A. Huber conducted the interviews, usually together.

The interviewees and the interview dates were:

Carol M. Anderson, PhD: October 25, 2006
G. Nicholas Beckwith III: September 1, 2005
George Board, DrPH: August 29, 2008 (telephone)
Charles E. Bogosta: February 12, 2007 (telephone)
Clifford E. Brubaker, PhD: March 31, 2006
Esther L. Bush: June 27, 2007
Hon. Ralph J. Cappy: December 21, 2005
Hon. Robert J. Cindrich: May 10, 2006
Elizabeth B. Concordia: April 20, 2007
J. Wray Connolly: January 24, 2006 (telephone)
Sandra N. Danoff: August 8, 2005; February 21, 2008 (telephone)
Leslie C. Davis: June 4, 2007
Lila Decker, RN: August 2, 2006
Robert A. DeMichiei: June 4, 2007
Thomas Detre, MD: January 27 (with George H. Taber), May 13, June 3, and November 17, 2005; January 30, July 24, October 5, December 20, and December 21, 2006
Dan Drawbaugh: January 26, 2007
Jane Duffield: July 20, 2005
Dean Eckenrode: September 7 and 19, 2006
David M. Farner: April 10, 2007
Bernard Fisher, MD: August 17, 2005
Philip Green: January 26, 2007 (telephone)
C. Talbot Heppenstall Jr.: June 20, 2007
Ronald B. Herberman, MD: October 3, 2005
Diane P. Holder: April 10, 2007
George A. Huber: August 18 and 22; October 7, 2005
Clyde B. Jones III: June 1, 2007
Edwin L. Klett: April 19, 2007
David J. Kupfer, MD: October 18, 2005
Scott Lammie: June 1, 2007
Mark J. Laskow: May 17, 2007 (telephone)
Gerald S. Levey, MD: February 21, 2006
Arthur S. Levine, MD: January 24, 2006
Jeffrey L. Masnick, MPH: September 8, 2008 (telephone)
David M. Matter: June 27, 2006
Margaret C. McDonald, PhD: May 11, 2006
John R. McGinley Jr.: March 18, 2008
Michele McKenney, MPH: August 29, 2008 (telephone)
George K. Michalopoulos, MD, PhD: June 28, 2005
Hon. John Murtha: August 7, 2006 (telephone)
Eugene N. Myers, MD, FACS: December 22, 2005
Mark A. Nordenberg: September 13, 2005
J. Dennis O'Connor, PhD: August 4, 2006
Roger A. Oxendale: June 20, 2007
Robert A. Paul: June 20, 2007 (telephone)
Gregory K. Peaslee: June 21, 2007
Hon. Edward G. Rendell: July 12, 2006
Jeffrey A. Romoff: May 5 and August 2, 2005; April 27 and August 2, 2006; January 23, 2007
Claudia Roth, PhD: June 21, 2007
Loren Roth, MD, MPH: August 9, 2005; April 13, 2007
Farrell Rubenstein: June 9, 2005
Ismail Sallam: October 17, 2006
Richard L. Simmons, MD: July 22, 2005
Thomas E. Starzl, MD, PhD: June 15, 2005
George H. Taber: January 27, 2005 (with Thomas Detre)
Robert C. Todd Jr.: April 5, 2006 (telephone)
Pamela Triolo, RN, PhD: June 27, 2007
Neil Van Horn: June 20, 2007
Marshall W. Webster, MD: June 29, 2005
George L. W. Werner: May 17, 2007 (telephone)
Donald D. Wolff Jr.: June 4, 2007
Leo W. Yochum: June 26, 2007
Julius S. Youngner, ScD: January 23, 2006
Mark L. Zeidel, MD: May 24, 2005

When the text clearly attributes a quotation by a person interviewed, there is no notation below. When the attribution is unclear or when the person quoted participated in the interview but was not the interviewee, there is a notation below. The usual notations for print and Internet sources appear below.

PREFACE

Page

7 *Some biologists believe*: E. G. Leigh Jr., and G. J. Vermeij, "Does Natural Selection Organize Ecosystems for the Maintenance of Higher Productivity and Diversity?" *Philosophical Transactions of the Royal Society of London* B257, 2002, 709–718.

CHAPTER 1: *Border Crossings*

Page

15 *"This was the question"*: Thomas Detre, MD, remarks at 65th Birthday Celebration (Pittsburgh, 1989), Detre Collection, Remarks, Lectures (Series 8), Health Sciences Library System, University of Pittsburgh.

15 *"the most successful"*: Herbert Y. Meltzer, in Herbert Y. Meltzer, MD, and Gary A. Gudelsky, PhD, "Clozapine: A Major Advance in the Treatment of Schizophrenia," in David J. Kupfer, ed., *Reflections on Modern Psychiatry* (Washington, DC: American Psychiatric Press, 1992), 103.

15 *"unique talent"*: Daniel X. Freedman, MD, "Summarizing Comments: The Past Predicts the Future," in *Reflections on Modern Psychiatry*, 120–121.

15 *"A man of"*: Maggie Scarf, "In the 'Therapeutic Community,' Patients Are Doctors," *New York Times Magazine*, May 25, 1969, http://select.nytimes.com/gst/abstract.html (accessed March 22, 2006).

15 *"bring down the tyranny"*: Romoff interview.

18 *"slightly stricter"*: "Detre Defined," *Pitt Medicine*, Fall–Winter 1998–1999, 4.

18 *"Anti-Semitism in Hungary"*: Thomas Detre, videotaped interview, Pittsburgh, PA, United States, 29 March 1998, Shoah Foundation Institute for Visual History and Education, University of Southern California.

18 *"The refugees arriving"*: Ibid.

19 *"This behavior"*: Ibid.

19 *"was largely random"*: "Detre Defined," 3.

19 *"a very profound sadness"*: Detre videotaped interview.

19 *"knack for"*: Freedman.

20 *"a little known"*: Thomas Detre, speech at Cornell Medical College, Psychiatry Department Retreat, 1991, Detre Collection, Remarks, Lectures (Series 8), Health Sciences Library System, University of Pittsburgh.

20 *"Psychotherapy alone"*: Thomas P. Detre and Henry G. Jarecki, MD, *Modern Psychiatric Treatment* (Philadelphia and Toronto: J. B. Lippincott Company, 1971), 521.

20 *"If all the crazies"*: Detre videotaped interview.

20 *"Darling"*: Ibid.

20 *"precise, amused voice"*: James Merrill, *A Different Person: A Memoir* (New York: Knopf, 1993), 206.

21 *"Tom was one of the first"*: Tom Crawford and Tommy Ehrbar, "In Good Health," *Pitt Magazine*, September 1998, 32.

23 *Luckily, Yale's chairman*: Susan Poppick, "Former Med. School Dean Redlich, 93, Passes Away," *Yale Daily News*, January 21, 2004, http://www.yaledailynews.com/articles/view/9641 (accessed May 3, 2006), and Calvin J. Frederick, Peter Loewenberg, and Robert O. Pasnau, *In Memoriam, Frederick C. Redlich*, http://www.universityofcalifornia.edu/senate/inmemoriam/FrederickC.Redlich.htm (accessed May 3, 2006).

23 *"a shining light"*: Letter from Thomas Detre to Dr. Lajos Angyal, April 12, 1962, Detre Collection, Early Years and Personal Files (Series 1), Health Sciences Library System, University of Pittsburgh, and Thomas Detre, personal interview, June 3, 2005.

23 *"The hospital is not"*: Scarf.

23 *"What did Thomas Detre"*: Freedman.

23 *"a gutsy kid"*: Kupfer interview.

26 *"insures the perpetual"*: R. R. Huggins, MD, "A Medical Center: Pittsburgh's Opportunity," brochure, Pittsburgh, July 1, 1922.

26 *"Such a wealth"*: Ibid.

26 *"to establish, maintain"*: Mary Brignano, *Gifts of a Family: The Richard King Mellon Philanthropies*, 1947–1997 (Pittsburgh, 1997), 56.

26 *In 1949 the University*: Marcia Kramer Schachner, "Western Psychiatric Institute and Clinic of the University of Pittsburgh: Its Years of Research, Teaching, and Service," doctoral dissertation, University of Pittsburgh, Pittsburgh, 1984, 102.

26 *"Pittsburgh has taken"*: Edwin Keister Jr., "Spock's Baby: The Famous Doc Nurtured Pittsburgh Children," *Pitt Med* 34, January 2002, 35.

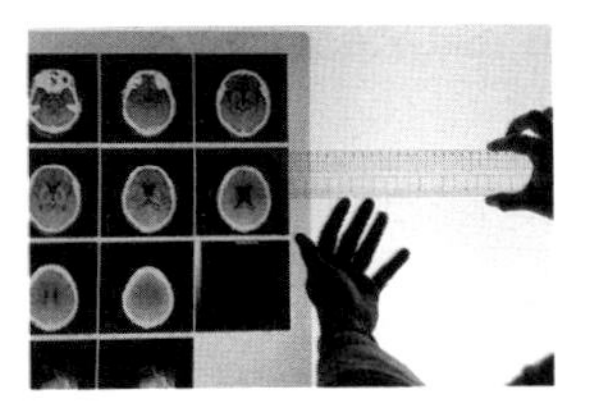

28 *In the Department of Psychiatry*: Detre interview. "Dr. Mirsky showed that people with high pepsinogen levels who were exposed to combat-related stress had a much higher chance to develop peptic ulcer," Detre explains. "So he was way ahead of his time."

28 *Dr. Brosin, meanwhile*: Schachner, 268.

28 *"reactionary, arrogant"*: Dr. Royden C. Astley to Dr. Henry W. Brosin, in Schachner, 269.

29 *By this time*: Schachner, 302.

CHAPTER 2: *The Leaders and Their Laboratory*

Page

34 *"There were no outstanding"*: In Schachner, 301.

34 *"for years without"*: Gerhard Werner, interviewed by Marcia Kramer Schachner. Ibid., 269.

34 *He envisioned a matrix*: Arthur S. Levine et al., "The Relationship Between the University of Pittsburgh School of Medicine and the University of Pittsburgh Medical Center – A Profile in Synergy," *Academic Medicine* 83, September 2008, 819, 821.

36 *Suddenly, the Pennsylvania*: Schachner, 297.

37 *"Tom recognized that if"*: Simmons interview. Dr. Detre and his colleagues were able to develop this important concept because of federal government policy for awarding research grants. Each grant has a direct cost and, added onto it, an indirect cost to cover the administrative and capital expenses to do the grant as well as such items as lab space, rent, telephone, etc. To determine the amount of these indirect costs, the federal government assigns each university an indirect cost rate based on its cost structure. If a university's indirect rate is 20 percent, it gets $1.20 for every grant dollar. If its indirect rate is 80 percent, it gets $1.80 for every dollar. Obviously, a high-cost structure is more advantageous to the university, and a university can raise its indirect cost rate by, for example, investing in such capital programs as research laboratories. (Dr. Detre would by 1991 drive the university's indirect cost rate at the medical center up to 49 percent.)

37 *"The University of Pittsburgh, like most"*: In Farner interview.

37 *"Good medicine"*: Thomas Detre, MD, speech given at Magee-Womens Hospital Spring 1987 Board of Directors Management Retreat, Pittsburgh, April 25, 1987, Detre Collection, Remarks, Lectures (Series 8), Health Sciences Library System, University of Pittsburgh.

38 *"a very small mental"*: Romoff interview.

43 *"We at Pitt"*: Schachner, 319.

44 *"The method for selecting"*: Thomas Detre, letter to Edison Montgomery, associate vice chancellor for the health professions, October 29, 1973, WPIC and Department of Psychiatry Records (Series 3), Detre Collection, Health Sciences Library System, University of Pittsburgh.

44 *"continued and vigorous"*: Thomas Detre, letter to F. S. Cheever, May 28, 1974, WPIC and Department of Psychiatry Records (Series 3), Detre Collection, Health Sciences Library System, University of Pittsburgh.

45 *"academicians who"*: Thomas Detre, speech given at Magee-Womens Hospital Spring 1987 Board of Directors Management Retreat.

45 *"Inter- and multi-disciplinarity"*: Arthur S. Levine, MD, "When You Come to a Fork in the Road, Take It," University of Pittsburgh School of Medicine 2007 State of the School Address, Pittsburgh, May 9, 2007, http://www.health.pitt.edu/state_of_the_school_address/2007/index.htm (accessed July 10, 2007).

46 *"He had an uncanny"*: Meyer Sonis, MD, *An Island Love Affair: A Family Memoir* (BookSurge Publishing, 2006), 380.

46 *"seven commandments"*: Thomas Detre, outline of a presentation on "Academic Health Center Management and Policy," University of Pittsburgh Graduate School of Public Health, October 21, 1987, Senior Vice Chancellor for the Health Sciences' Office Records (Series 4), Detre Collection, Health Sciences Library System, University of Pittsburgh.

50 *"boot camps"*: Bernard Wysocki Jr., "At Pitt, Scientists Decode the Secret of Getting Grants," *Wall Street Journal Online*, June 28, 2004: Page One Feature, http://webreprints.djreprints.com/1041931195462.html (accessed July 14, 2005).

51 *And a front-page*: Ibid.

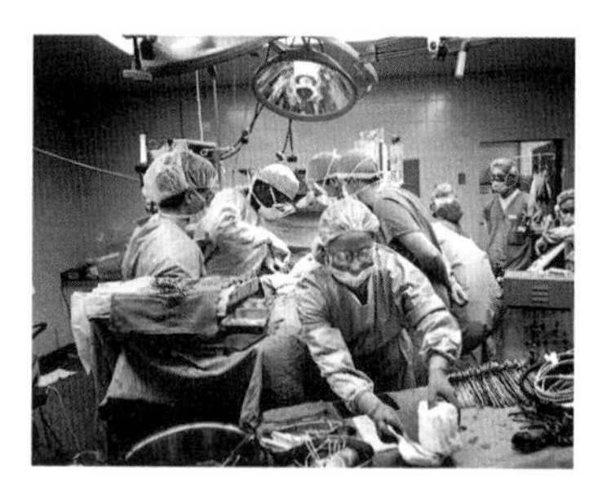

CHAPTER 3: *A New Ecology*

Page

55 *Tom Detre got the jump*: In Crawford and Ehrbar, "In Good Health," 32.

56 *"Part pragmatist"*: Quoted in Mike Crawmer, "Health Sciences Test Detre's Skills as a Manager," *University Times*, 17, 9, January 24, 1985, 3.

57 *"I don't catch anything"*: "Detre Defined," 6.

57 *"mobilize its fiscal"*: Thomas Detre, letter to George H. Taber, vice president and director, Richard King Mellon Foundation, September 8, 1983, Senior Vice Chancellor for the Health Sciences' Office Records (Series 4), Detre Collection, Health Sciences Library System, University of Pittsburgh.

58 *"the financial and moral power"*: Ibid.

58 *"great academic medical center"*: Huggins.

62 *"totally overlooked"*: Thomas Detre, letter to George Taber.

63 *"thus assuring equal"*: Ibid.

63 *"to participate in the creation"*: Ibid.

64 *"I believe that a private"*: Ibid.

64 *In December 1983*: The Richard King Mellon Foundation would provide an additional $3 million in 1986 and another $8 million in 1989 for further development of programmatic activities and for construction of laboratory facilities for the Pittsburgh Cancer Institute.

66 *"persistence"*: Detre interview.

66 *"The very generous grants"*: Thomas Detre, letter to George Taber, September 18, 1989, Senior Vice Chancellor for the Health Sciences' Office Records (Series 4), Detre Collection, Health Sciences Library System, University of Pittsburgh.

67 *Rumors about "infighting"*: Barbara I. Paull, *A Century of Medical Excellence: The History of the University of Pittsburgh School of Medicine* (Pittsburgh, 1986), 247, and Mark Roth, "Infighting Behind Changes at Pitt?" *Pittsburgh Post-Gazette*, July 12, 1984, 4.

67 *"The real story"*: Mark Roth.

68 *"The university had the best"*: Minutes of the Senate Council Meeting of November 5, 1984, University Senate, University of Pittsburgh. Courtesy of The Senate of the University of Pittsburgh.

68 *"The basic science researcher"*: Thomas Detre, "The Future of Research in Academic Departments," panel on "Managed Care + Academic Careers = Managed Academic Careers," Annual Meeting of the Association of University Anesthesiologists, May 19, 1995, Detre Collection, Remarks, Lectures (Series 8), Health Sciences Library System, University of Pittsburgh.

70 *"upper" and "lower"*: Crawmer, 3.

70 *Professors in the medical*: Mike Pellegrini, "Faculty at 5 Pitt Schools Fear Merger," *Pittsburgh Post-Gazette*, March 12, 1985, 8.

70 *"catastrophic neglect"*: Detre letter to George Taber, September 18, 1989.

CHAPTER 4: *Consolidating*

Page

77 *"stimulate, expropriate"*: Loren Roth interview.

77 *"The UHCP hospitals"*: Detre letter to George Taber, September 8, 1983.

80 *"has not consistently"*: Presbyterian-University Hospital Concept Paper, Approved by Presbyterian-University Hospital Executive Committee and Recommended with Revision to the Board of Trustees, June 25, 1986. UPMC archives.

80 *"A university hospital's"*: Thomas Detre, Carnegie Mellon University Mental Health Policy Colloquium Series, 1982, Detre Collection, Remarks, Lectures (Series 8), Health Sciences Library System, University of Pittsburgh.

80 *"The university is no longer"*: "Pitt to Leave Health Center," *Pittsburgh Press*, March 31, 1983, C-8.

80 *"Apparently everyone"*: Editorial, "Pitt's Impossible Dream," *Pittsburgh Post-Gazette*, April 6, 1983, A-6.

82 *"this is the hottest"*: Lindsey Gruson, "Center for Transplants Aids Pittsburgh Ascent," *New York Times*, September 16, 1985, A-10.

82 *But Presby was running*: Simmons interview and Myers interview.

84 *"furious"*: Detre and Taber interview.

85 *"This was kind of like"*: The Eye & Ear Foundation of Pittsburgh is an independent, not-for-profit supporting foundation; its principal mission is support for the departments of Otolaryngology and Ophthalmology at the University of Pittsburgh and UPMC.

85 *"Which was very important"*: In Rubenstein interview.

85 *"best efforts"*: Jack E. Freeman letter to David Goff, July 26, 1985. UPMC archives.

87 *"That was a key issue"*: In Detre and Taber interview.

87 *"They said they were not"*: Ibid. and Detre interview.

88 *"to unite the leadership"*: Presbyterian-University Hospital Concept Paper.

90 *"just about a shoot-out"*: Huber in Detre interview.

90 *"As it was in 1930"*: Presbyterian-University Hospital Concept Paper. UPMC archives.

93 *To sort out*: Carol Stein Bleier with Lu Donnelly and Samuel P. Granowitz, MD, *L'Chaim, To Good Health and Life: A History of Montefiore Hospital of Pittsburgh, Pennsylvania*, 1898–1990 (Pittsburgh, 1997), 253.

95 *Interestingly, one of the*: Huber, in Rubenstein interview.

95 *"precipitously, thereby excluding"*: Len Boselovic, "Hospital Sues Partner," *Pittsburgh Press*, March 21, 1991: C-7, and Bruce Steele, "HealthAmerica and Blue Cross Skirmish Over Physician Deals," *University Times* 27 (11), February 2, 1995, http://mac10.umc.pitt.edu (accessed June 3, 2006).

95 *"And [then] HealthAmerica"*: In Rubenstein interview.

95 *"With your help"*: Thomas Detre, letter to George H. Taber, vice president and director, Richard King Mellon Foundation, June 19, 1990, Senior Vice Chancellor for the Health Sciences' Office Records (Series 4), Detre Collection, Health Sciences Library System, University of Pittsburgh.

CHAPTER 5: *Transitions*

Page

100 *"Jeff is a little like"*: In 2005 Dr. Zeidel was appointed the Herrman Ludwig Blumgart Professor of Medicine at Harvard Medical School and physician-in-chief and chairman of the Department of Medicine at Boston's Beth Israel Deaconess Medical Center.

105 *"Pitt medical beast"*: Mary Pat Flaherty, "Mosque Fiasco Shows Need to Tame Pitt Medical Beast," *Pittsburgh Press*, June 9, 1991, A-2.

105 *"It was an interesting time"*: "I never felt that way," Nordenberg added. "Of course, I was viewing things as a faculty member with broader portfolio or no special knowledge, but I always thought that medicine was the highest calling, that when you did have such strength and commitment to excellence in medicine within an institution, it was something that ought to be a source of real pride."

107 *The president of the faculty*: "Pitt Faculty to Probe Medical Center Appointment," October 7, 1992: A-6. *The Allegheny Bulletin* was a publication of The Pittsburgh Press Company produced during a newspaper strike which disrupted publication of *The Pittsburgh Press*, http://infoweb.newsbank.com (accessed June 2, 2006).

108 *"Over the past decade"*: Thomas Detre, speech given to Chinese Ambassador's Delegation, Pittsburgh, February 25, 1994, Detre Collection, Remarks, Lectures (Series 8), Health Sciences Library System, University of Pittsburgh.

CHAPTER 6: *Beyond Oakland*

Page

113 *"We are undergoing"*: Jeffrey A. Romoff, "The Transformation of the Academic Medical Center: The Managed Care Marketplace and the Future of the UPMC," November 15, 1995, UPMC archives.

113 *"economic restructuring"*: Rick Mayes and Robert A. Berenson, *Medicare Prospective Payment and the Shaping of U.S. Health Care* (Baltimore: The Johns Hopkins University Press, 2006), 2, http://www.press.jhu.edu/books/title_pages/3463.html (accessed June 3, 2007).

113 *"the lowest level of expense"*: Eckenrode interview, September 7, 2006.

114 *High-cost academic*: Henry J. Aaron, "The Plight of Academic Medical Centers," Policy Brief No. 59, The Brookings Institution, May 2000, 2, http://www.brookings.edu/ (accessed January 16, 2006).

114 *"will condemn our citizens"*: Thomas Detre, "Why We Can't Do Without Academic Medical Centers," Detre Collection. Remarks, Lectures (Series 8), Health Sciences Library System, University of Pittsburgh.

114 *"huge, looming threat"*: Michalopoulos interview.

114 *So AGH crossed...in the country*: Interestingly, Shadyside Hospital also came close to an affiliation with a medical school in western Ohio in order to protect its residency programs, according to Mark Laskow (Laskow interview).

114 *"The CEO of the"*: Detre interview. Dr. Detre also predicted the collapse of AHERF. "I thought the economic offers they made to incoming faculty were beyond any impulse of rationality. I said, 'You know, this is dangerous, and eventually this place is going to go under.'"

115 *"The basic premise is that"*: Thomas Detre and Jeffrey A. Romoff letter to George H. Taber and Andrew W. Mathieson, November 15, 1988.

115 *"We had great concern"*: In Danoff interview.

117 *"beyond the walls"*: Huber, in Danoff interview.

117 *"John Paul told me"*: In Loren Roth interview.

118 *"when the university uses"*: Jeffrey A. Romoff, Letters, "UPMC, the Medical School and University Health Care Plan," *University Times* 27 (11), February 2, 1995, 2.

118 *Detractors of UPMC*: Bruce Steele and Mike Sajna, "Faculty, Staff Reactions to News of Resignation Run the Gamut," *University Times* 27 (16), April 13, 1995, 1, 5.

118 *"Jeffrey Romoff...made it clear"*: Editorial, "Health-Care Fever: Pitt Medical Center Moves Illustrate a National Trend," *Pittsburgh Post-Gazette*, March 1, 1996, A-20.

118 *"In a competitive"*: Ibid.

118 *"throw keys"*: CEO Strategy Meeting Notes, April 5, 1996. Courtesy of David Farner.

118 *"The window of opportunity"*: Ibid.

118 *"John put a lot"*: In Danoff interview.

121 *"an earth-shattering"*: Beckwith interview.

121 *"rational construct"*: Romoff interview.

122 *"We wanted this network"*: Mary Brignano, *The Story of St. Margaret* (Pittsburgh: UPMC St. Margaret, 1998), 103.

129 *"What UPMC's creators"*: Arthur S. Levine et al., "The Relationship Between the University of Pittsburgh School of Medicine and the University of Pittsburgh Medical Center – A Profile in Synergy," *Academic Medicine* 83, 9, September 2008, 821.

132 *Passavant served a formal*: Pamela Gaynor, "Passavant Not Happy with UPMC Merger," *Pittsburgh Post-Gazette*, November 23, 1999, F-1; Pamela Gaynor, "Passavant Lays Out Rationale for Divorce," *Pittsburgh Post-Gazette*, March 21, 2000, F-1; Jane-Ellen Robinet, "A Crack in the Armor: DeStefano Leads Charge to Leave UPMC," *Pittsburgh Business Times*, March 27, 2000, http://pittsburgh.bizjournals.com/ (accessed July 10, 2007).

CHAPTER 7: *Reinventing UPMC*

Page

139 *"re-engineer the delivery"*: Lammie interview.

139 *And even though clinical*: Bowman, Marjorie A., MD, MPA; Arthur H. Rubenstein, MBBCh; Arthur S. Levine, MD, "Clinical Revenue Investment in Biomedical Research: Lessons from Two Academic Medical Centers," *Journal of the American Medical Association* 297 (22), June 13, 2007, 2523.

141 *"'Look,'" John said"*: In Eckenrode interview.

141 *"People would ask us"*: Ibid.

142 *"because of the state's"*: Pamela Gaynor, "Mating Season in Full Bloom," *Pittsburgh Post-Gazette*, October 27, 1995, C-1, http://infoweb.newsbank.com (accessed August 7, 2007).

145 *"Academic medical centers"*: Martin Van Der Werf, "Changing Economics of Health Care Are Devastating Academic Medical Centers," *Chronicle of Higher Education*, May 21, 1999, A-38; Katherine S. Mangan, "Off the Critical List," *Chronicle of Higher Education*, January 31, 2003, Money and Management, A-27–A-28; and Henry J. Aaron, ed., "Future of Academic Medical Centers," Washington, DC: Brookings Institution Press, 2001, 8, http://www.brookings.edu (accessed June 23, 2008).

147 *"respond more efficiently"*: Bruce Steele, "Clinical Practice Plans Being Merged into Single Plan," *University Times* 29 (19), May 29, 1997, http://www.umc.pitt.edu/utimes/ (accessed August 6, 2007).

147 *UPMC already provided $50 million*: Bruce Steele, "Administrators Discuss Unified Practice Plan," *University Times* 30 (13), March 5, 1998, http://www.umc.pitt.edu/utimes/ (accessed August 6, 2007).

147 *"if UPMC and its"*: Bruce Steele, "Adler Says His Forced Resignation Is Not the Issue in Pitt Med School," *University Times* 30 (12), February 19, 1998, http://www.umc.pitt.edu/utimes/ (accessed August 6, 2007).

148 *they also subsidized*: Paull, 250.

148 *"each practice plan"*: In Webster interview.

148 *"In the past, when an outside"*: In Bruce Steele, "Clinical Practice Plans Being Merged into Single Plan," *University Times* 29 (19), May 29, 1997, http://www.umc.pitt.edu/utimes/ (accessed August 6, 2007).

148 *"Darth Vader"*: Bruce Steele, "Adler Says His Forced Resignation Is Not the Issue."

148 *"takeover of the Pitt practice"*: Bruce Steele, "Medical Profs to Elect Committee to Represent Faculty's Interests," *University Times* 30 (16), April 16, 1998, http://www.umc.pitt.edu/utimes/ (accessed August 6, 2007).

148 *"despite its close links"*: Gordon MacLeod, in "Senate Matters," *University Times* 30 (13), March 5, 1998, http://www.umc.pitt.edu/utimes/ (accessed August 6, 2007).

149 *"compliance with rules"*: Association of American Medical Colleges, Physicians at Teaching Hospitals (PATH) Audits, http://www.aamc.org (accessed June 23, 2008).

151 *"is more attractive to me"*: In Bill Schackner, "NIH Scientist to Head Pitt's Health Schools," *Pittsburgh Post-Gazette*, May 22, 1998, B-1, http://infoweb.newsbank.com (accessed August 3, 2007).

153 *"long, emotional"*: Oxendale interview.

153 *"A firestorm of questions"*: Pamela Gaynor, "Did It Have a Choice?" *Pittsburgh Post-Gazette*, April 24, 2001, E-1, http://infoweb.newsbank.com (accessed August 2, 2007).

155 *Highmark filed a federal lawsuit*: Emily J. Tipping, "Appraising the Children's–UPMC Merger," *Physician's News Digest*, December 2001, http://physiciansnews.com (accessed August 2, 2007); and Pamela Gaynor, "Insurers Sue to Stop Merger – Highmark, Allies Claim UPMC, Children's Deal Illegal," *Pittsburgh Post-Gazette*, June 20, 2001, A-1, http://infoweb.newsbank.com (accessed August 2, 2007).

155 *"Completely wrong"*: In Pamela Gaynor, "Children's Deal Clears Hurdle," *Pittsburgh Post-Gazette*, July 20, 2001, C-12, http://infoweb.newsbank.com (accessed August 2, 2007).

155 *"as a back door"*: Pamela Gaynor, "UPMC Steps Up Merger Attack," *Pittsburgh Post-Gazette*, April 16, 1999, A-1, http://infoweb.newsbank.com (accessed August 3, 2007); and Pamela Gaynor, "UPMC Sues Highmark, West Penn and State," *Pittsburgh Post-Gazette*, February 17, 2000, F-1, http://infoweb.newsbank.com (accessed August 3, 2007).

155 *Without a new Highmark contract*: Len Boselovic, "Highmark Threatens UPMC High Debt Rating," *Pittsburgh Post-Gazette*, March 19, 2002, E-4, http://infoweb.newsbank.com (accessed July 13, 2007).

155 *"was always a brinksman"*: Farner interview and Oxendale interview.

155 *UPMC threatened to end*: Pamela Gaynor, "Highmark, UPMC Finally Strike a Deal," *Pittsburgh Post-Gazette*, June 27, 2002, A-1, http://infoweb.newsbank.com (accessed July 13, 2007).

155 *"Extortion"*: Pamela Gaynor, "St. Francis Deal Makes Partners Out of UPMC and Highmark; Some Wonder If Consumers Will Benefit," *Pittsburgh Post-Gazette*, August 20, 2002, E-1; and "Coming Together – UPMC Hammers Out Deals With Highmark, Children's and St. Francis in Year of Consolidation," *Pittsburgh Post-Gazette*, December 27, 2002, B-7, http://infoweb.newsbank.com (accessed July 13, 2007).

155 *On a taped local television*: Christopher Snowbeck, "Romoff Calls Highmark 'Ticket Scalpers' – UPMC Chief's Remarks on Television Taping Increase Heat in Contract Dispute," *Pittsburgh Post-Gazette*, May 4, 2002, A-7, http://infoweb.newsbank.com (accessed July 13, 2007).

156 *"Why not come together"*: Gaynor, "Coming Together – UPMC Hammers Out Deals with Highmark, Children's and St. Francis in Year of Consolidation."

156 *"a blessing for the whole community"*: In Teresa F. Lindeman, "St. Francis to Close – Children's Moving In," *Pittsburgh Post-Gazette*, August 20, 2002, A-1, http://infoweb.newsbank.com (accessed July 13, 2007).

156 *I had represented to the bishop*: The Most Reverend Donald W. Wuerl, STD, was installed in 2006 as Archbishop of Washington, DC.

157 *"The convergence of interests"*: Editorial, "Healthy Convergence – Making the Most of the St. Francis–Children's Deal," *Pittsburgh Post-Gazette*, August 21, 2002, A-14, http://infoweb.newsbank.com (accessed July 13, 2007).

158 *"It would be very hard"*: In Michael Yablonski, "Mother Superior," *Pittsburgh Professional Magazine*, August 2007: 14.

159 *"pillar of Pittsburgh"*: C. Hax McCullough Jr. and Mary Brignano, *Pillar of Pittsburgh: The History of Mercy Hospital and the City It Serves* (Pittsburgh, 1990).

159 *"We conducted a thoughtful"*: Sister Margaret Hannan, "The Merger with UPMC Saved Mercy Hospital," *Pittsburgh Post-Gazette*, November 1, 2006, B-7, http://infoweb.newsbank.com (accessed February 21, 2008).

160 *"There is one fundamental"*: Robert P. Lockwood, "What Does It Mean to Be a Catholic Hospital?" *UPMC Extra!* February 8, 2008.

160 *"What do you need?"* Danoff telephone interview, February 21, 2008.

162 *Sister Hannan said the fund*: Mark Belko, "Mercy Joins UPMC – Hospital Officials Say Quality of Care Will Continue," *Pittsburgh Post-Gazette*, January 4, 2008, F-1, http://infoweb.newsbank.com/ (accessed February 21, 2008).

162 Ibid.

162 *After reviewing tens of thousands*: Chuck Moody, "Mercy's Transfer to UPMC Moves Ahead," *Pittsburgh Catholic*, October 22, 2007, http://www.pittsburghcatholic.org/newsarticles/ (accessed March 18, 2008).

163 *"You have taken a 160-year…in your ministry"*: Belko.

CHAPTER 8: *A Culture of Hunger*

Page

171 *"in fairly large numbers"*: In 1987 the United Network for Organ Sharing (UNOS) would adopt a system developed at the University of Pittsburgh that directed organs to the sickest patients first, regardless of where they were from, but limited foreign recipients to a percentage of donated organs.

174 *"If we want everything"*: Giuseppe di Lampedusa, *The Leopard*, trans. Archibald Colquhoun (New York: Pantheon Books, 1960), 40.

174 *Each year the University*: Dipartimento Interaziendale per I Trapianti e Terapie ad Alta Specializzazione: Economic Impact Study and Business Plan, 1997. UPMC archives.

175 *"I was happy when McDonald's"*: In Laurie McGinley, "Leading a Renaissance: Sicily Pegs Hope for Better Care, Economic Revival on Joint Transplant Venture with UPMC," *Wall Street Journal*, February 14, 2000, A-1, http://web.LexisNexis.com (accessed December 5, 2006).

175 *"a gesture of"*: In Phil Davison, "Cardinal Salvatore Pappalardo, Anti-Mafia Sicilian Priest," *Independent*, Obituaries, December 14, 2006, http://www.independent.co.uk (accessed April 26, 2008).

176 *"a complicated culture"*: Ian Fisher, "Breaking All the Rules, with a Shrug and a Sigh," *New York Times*, February 14, 2007, A-4, national edition.

177 *"If most Italians manage"*: Luigi Barzini, *The Italians: A Full-Length Portrait Featuring Their Manners and Morals* (New York: Bantam Books, 1964), 253.

178 *"in a manner which is consistent"*: Dipartimento Interaziendale per I Trapianti e Terapie ad Alta Specializzazione, UPMC archives, 85.

178 *"the most sophisticated clinical"*: Romoff interview.

179 *"the expressions on the faces"*: Ignazio R. Marino, letter to Thomas Detre, July 13, 1996, Detre Collection, UPMC International Programs (Series 5), Health Sciences Library System, University of Pittsburgh.

182 *"an enterprise of heroic proportions"*: Barzini.

184 *When critics attacked the cost*: UPMC Health System Statement on Financial Relationship with Istituto Mediterraneo per I Trapianti e Terapie ad Alta Specializzazione, Draft of April 16, 1999, quoting R. H. Hauboldt, *Cost Implications of Human Organ and Tissue Transplantations, an Update*: 1996, Research Report published by Milliman & Robertson, Inc., 1997, Detre Collection, UPMC International Programs (Series 5), Health Sciences Library System, University of Pittsburgh; and Laurie McGinley, "Leading a Renaissance."

185 *"They're lucky they got"*: Luis Fabregas, "UPMC Gives Hope, Draws Fire in Italy," *Pittsburgh Tribune-Review*, October 17, 2004, http://www.pittsburghlive.com (accessed January 3, 2007).

185 *"currently the most"*: Laurie McGinley.

185 *"When you mentioned Palermo"*: Michael Woods, "UPMC International – Sicilian Institute Has Done Hundreds of Transplants; Plans Shape Up for Irish, Middle Eastern Units," *Pittsburgh Post-Gazette*, March 13, 2005, D-1.

CHAPTER 9: *UPMC in a New Key*

Page

194 *With the terrorist attacks*: Levine, University of Pittsburgh School of Medicine 2007 State of the School Address.

195 *"In the U.S."*: Jeffrey A. Romoff, videotaped interview, 2006, UPMC archives.

195 *"flattened"*: Thomas L. Friedman, *The World Is Flat: A Brief History of the Twenty-First Century* (New York: Farrar, Strauss and Giroux, 2005).

197 *"Pittsburgh has not been built"*: Theodore Roosevelt, Address to the Board of Directors of the Chamber of Commerce of Pittsburgh in the William Penn Hotel, July 25, 1919, in John Pryor Cowan, ed., *Great Men, Their Esteem for a Great City* (Pittsburgh, 1919), 15.

201 *"a landmark agreement"*: Cinda Becker and Joseph Conn, "Forward March: IBM Strengthens Healthcare Presence through UPMC, Healthlink Deals," *Modern Healthcare*, May 2, 2005, 25, http://web.LexisNexis.com/ (accessed December 19, 2006).

201 *"eye-opening megadeal"*: Bob Evans, "Business Technology: The Real Impact of the IBM–UPMC Deal." *InformationWeek* (May 2, 2005): 72 http://www.informationweek.com/shared/printableArticleSrc.jhtml?articleID=162100327 (accessed on May 23, 2005).

202 *"use our resource to effect"*: Jeffrey A. Romoff, speech given at UPMC Board Retreat, Pittsburgh, November 14, 2006, UPMC archives.

CHAPTER 10: *Look Back … and Imagine the Future*

Page

208 *When Detre and Romoff came*: Dan Fitzpatrick, "Top of the Triangle: UPMC Getting Ready to Put Its Name on U.S. Steel Tower," *Pittsburgh Post-Gazette*, April 25, 2008, E-1.

211 *In what is believed:* "$100 Million Commitment by the University of Pittsburgh Medical Center to Fund Post-Secondary Education for Pittsburgh's High School Graduates." UPMC Media Relations, December 5, 2007.

215 *"To summarize"*: Levine, University of Pittsburgh School of Medicine 2007 State of the School Address.

SELECTED SOURCES

Aaron, Henry J. "The Plight of Academic Medical Centers." Policy Brief No. 59, The Brookings Institution (May 2000), http://www.brookings.edu/ (accessed on January 16, 2006).

———, ed. "Future of Academic Medical Centers." Washington, DC: Brookings Institution Press, 2001.

———. "The Rising Cost of Health Care: Is It a Problem?" Remarks to the 2004 Annual Meeting, Institute of Medicine.

Adler, Gerald, MD. "Modern Psychiatric Treatment" (review). *Annals of Internal Medicine* 75 (October 1971): 651–652.

Alberts, Robert C. *Pitt: The Story of the University of Pittsburgh,* 1787–1987. Pittsburgh: University of Pittsburgh Press, 1986.

"Arthur Levine." *University Times* 30 (May 28, 1998), http://mac10.umc.pitt.edu/ (accessed on June 16, 2006).

Association of American Medical Colleges. Physicians At Teaching Hospitals (PATH) Audits, Summary. http://www.aamc.org/ (accessed on June 23, 2008).

Baker, Stephen. "Who Gets a Liver—And Who Doesn't." *Business Week* 3505 (December 9, 1996): 153.

Baker, Stephen, and Monica Larner. "Transplanting the Transplant Biz." *Business Week* 3503 (November 25, 1996): 128.

Barzini, Luigi. *The Italians: A Full-Length Portrait Featuring Their Manners and Morals.* New York: Bantam Books, 1964.

Becker, Cinda, and Joseph Conn. "Forward March: IBM Strengthens Healthcare Presence through UPMC, Healthlink Deals." *Modern Healthcare* 25 (May 2, 2005), http://web.LexisNexis.com (accessed on December 19, 2006).

Belko, Mark. "Mercy Joins UPMC — Hospital Officials Say Quality of Care Will Continue." *Pittsburgh Post-Gazette* (January 4, 2008): F-1, http://infoweb.newsbank.com (accessed on February 21, 2008).

Billiar, Timothy R., MD, and Andrew B. Peitzman, MD. "The Department of Surgery at the School of Medicine at the University of Pittsburgh, Pittsburgh, PA." *Archives of Surgery* 139 (May 2004).

Bleier, Carol Stein, with Lu Donnelly and Samuel P. Granowitz, MD. *L'Chaim, To Good Health and Life: A History of Montefiore Hospital of Pittsburgh, Pennsylvania, 1898–1990.* Pittsburgh, 1997.

Boselovic, Len. "Hospital Sues Partner." *Pittsburgh Press* (March 21, 1991) C-7.

Bowman, Marjorie A.; Arthur H. Rubenstein; and Arthur S. Levine. "Clinical Revenue Investment in Biomedical Research: Lessons from Two Academic Medical Centers." *Journal of the American Medical Association* 297 (June 13, 2007): 2521–2524.

Brignano, Mary. *Gifts of a Family: The Richard King Mellon Philanthropies,* 1947–1997. Pittsburgh, 1997.

———. *Inheritors of a Glorious Reality: A History of Shadyside Hospital.* Pittsburgh, 1991.

———. *The Story of St. Margaret.* Pittsburgh, 1997.

Burns, Lawton R., John Cacciamani, James Clement, and Welman Aquino. "The Fall of the House of AHERF: The Allegheny Bankruptcy." *Health Affairs* 19 (Jan/Feb 2000): 7–41.

Catholic Health East. "Pittsburgh Mercy Health System Signs Letter of Intent to Transfer Ownership of The Mercy Hospital of Pittsburgh to UPMC." (September 20, 2006), http://www.che.org (accessed on April 21, 2008).

"Changing the Face of Medicine, Dr. Katherine M. Detre." United States Library of Health, National Institutes of Health. http://www.nlm.nih.gov

Chielli, Jack J., and Jeffrey Barg. "MDs Confront Highmark & UPMC." *Physician's News Digest* (August 1998), http://www.physiciansnews.com (accessed on May 21, 2008).

Cowan, John Pryor, ed. *Great Men, Their Esteem for a Great City.* Pittsburgh, 1919.

Crawford, Tom, and Tommy Ehrbar. "In Good Health." *Pitt Magazine* (September 1998): 30–34.

Crawmer, Mike. "Health Sciences Test Detre's Skills as a Manager." *University Times,* 17, 9 (January 24, 1985): 3.

Culbertson R. "How Successfully Can Academic Faculty Practices Compete in Developing Managed Care Markets?" *Academic Medicine* 71 (1996): 858–870.

Davison, Phil. "Cardinal Salvatore Pappalardo, Anti-Mafia Sicilian Priest." *The Independent,* Obituaries (December 14, 2006), http://www.independent.co.uk/news/obituaries/cardinal-salvatore-pappalardo-428341.html (accessed on December 19, 2006).

Detre, Thomas P., MD, FAPA, and Henry G. Jarecki, MD. *Modern Psychiatric Treatment.* Philadelphia and Toronto: J. B. Lippincott Company, 1971.

———. Reports to Richard King Mellon Foundation, 1983–1996.

"Detre Defined." *Pitt Medicine* (Fall–Winter 1998–1999): 2–7.

Di Lampedusa, Giuseppe. *The Leopard.* Trans. Archibald Colquhoun. New York: Pantheon Books, 1960.

Encyclopedia Britannica. "Kraepelin, Emil." Encyclopedia Britannica Online (16 March 2006). http://search.eb/article-9046179.

Evans, Bob. "Business Technology: The Real Impact of the IBM–UPMC Deal." *InformationWeek* (May 2, 2005): 72, http://www.informationweek.com (accessed on May 23, 2005).

Fabregas, Luis. "UPMC Gives Hope, Draws Fire in Italy." *Pittsburgh Tribune-Review* (October 17, 2004), http://www.pittsburghlive.com (accessed on January 4, 2007).

Fisher, Ian. "Breaking All the Rules, with a Shrug and a Sigh." *New York Times* (February 14, 2007): A-4.

Fitzpatrick, Dan. "Top of the Triangle: UPMC Getting Ready to Put Its Name on U. S. Steel Tower." *Pittsburgh Post-Gazette* (April 25, 2008): E-1.

Frederick, Calvin J., Peter Loewenberg, and Robert O. Pasnau. *In Memoriam, Frederick C. Redlich.* http://www.universityofcalifornia.edu/senate/ (accessed on May 3, 2006).

Friedman, Thomas L. *The World Is Flat: A Brief History of the Twenty-First Century.* New York: Farrar, Strauss and Giroux, 2005.

Gaynor, Pamela. "Shadyside Joins Pitt Colossus." *Pittsburgh Post-Gazette* (June 6, 1996): Business A-1, http://infoweb.newsbank.com (accessed on April 22, 2007).

———. "Health Plans Getting Narrower." *Pittsburgh Post-Gazette* (October 11, 1996): B-1, http://infoweb.newsbank.com (accessed on April 22, 2007).

———. "UPMC Wooing Blue Cross." *Pittsburgh Post-Gazette* (June 20, 1997): A-1, http://infoweb.newsbank.com (accessed on April 22, 2007).

———. "St. Francis Deal Makes Partners Out of UPMC and Highmark; Some Wonder If Consumers Will Benefit." *Pittsburgh Post-Gazette* (August 20, 2002): E-1.

Gruson, Leslie. "Center for Transplants Aids Pittsburgh Ascent." *New York Times* (September 16, 1985): A-10.

Hannan, Sister Margaret. "The Merger with UPMC Saved Mercy Hospital." *Pittsburgh Post-Gazette* (November 1, 2006): B-7, http://infoweb.newsbank.com (accessed on February 21, 2008).

Harden, Victoria A. "National Institutes of Health." *The Oxford Companion to United States History.* Paul S. Boyer, ed. Oxford University Press 2001. *Oxford Reference Online.* Oxford University Press. The Pennsylvania State University Library – Penn State. http://www.oxfordreference.com (accessed on June 24, 2008).

Healy, David. "A Dance to the Music of the Century: Changing Fashions in 20th-Century Psychiatry." The Royal College of Psychiatrists, *Psychiatric Bulletin* 24 (2000), http://pb.rcpsych.org (accessed on April 20, 2006).

Healy, Patrick. "Teaching Hospitals Are Relieved by Collapse of Commission Studying Medicare." *Chronicle of Higher Education* 45 (March 26, 1999): A-40.

Herberman, Ronald B. "Translation of Scientific Insights to Benefit Patients with Cancer." *Cancer Biology and Therapy* 3 (August 2004): 778–781.

"Hospital/Departmental Collaboration: New Paradigm for an Unnatural Act; Conversations with Mark (Zeidel, MD)." PowerPoint Presentation, 2004 APM Winter Meeting (February 2004).

Huggins, R. R., MD. "A Medical Center: Pittsburgh's Opportunity." Pittsburgh, July 1, 1922.

Jefferson, Margo. "Abroad in the 50's, Finding the Way to be a Poet." *New York Times,* Books of the Times (September 15, 1993), http://query.nytimes.com (accessed on April 3, 2006).

Keister, Edwin Jr. "Dramatic Landing: Freud, Biology, and the History of a Psychiatry Powerhouse." *Pitt Med* 4 (April 2002): 28–33.

———. "Spock's Baby: The Famous Doc Nurtured Pittsburgh Children." *Pitt Med* 4 (January 2002): 35.

———. "A Hospital Is Born." *Pitt Med* 5 (May 2003): 17–19.

Kidney, Walter C. "UHCP Toward a Unified Medical Center." *Pittsburgher Magazine* (April 1979).

Kupfer, David J., ed. *Reflections on Modern Psychiatry.* Washington, DC: American Psychiatric Press, 1992.

Lane, David. "Palermo Polishes Its Image: Sicily's Capital Is Struggling to Repair the Wounds of War and Mafia Murders." *Financial Times* (March 2, 2002): 2.

Leigh, E. G. Jr., and G. J. Vermeij. "Does Natural Selection Organize Ecosystems for the Maintenance of Higher Productivity and Diversity?" *Philosophical Transactions of the Royal Society of London* B257 (2002): 709–718.

Levin, Steve. "Empire Building." 5-part series. *Pittsburgh Post-Gazette* (December 25–30, 2005).

Levine, A. S.; Detre, T. P.; McDonald, M. C.; Roth, L. H.; Huber, G. A.; Brignano, M. G.; Danoff, S. N.; Farner, D. M.; Masnick, J. L.; Romoff, J. A. "The Relationship Between the University of Pittsburgh School of Medicine and the University of Pittsburgh Medical Center – A Profile in Synergy." *Academic Medicine* 83, 9 (September 2008): 816–826.

Levine, Arthur S. "Strengths, Threats, and Opportunities: Strategies for Dealing with Tough Times in Academic Medicine." University of Pittsburgh School of Medicine 2006 State of the School Address (May 10, 2006).

———. "When You Come to a Fork in the Road, Take It." University of Pittsburgh School of Medicine 2007 State of the School Address (May 9, 2007). http://www.health.pitt.edu (accessed on July 10, 2007).

Lockwood, Robert P. "Mercy Hospital: How It Will Stay Catholic." *Pittsburgh Catholic* (December 12, 2004), http://www.pittsburgh catholic.org (accessed on March 18, 2008).

———. "What Does It Mean To Be a Catholic Hospital?" *UPMC Extra!* (February 8, 2008): 3.

Magill, M. K., A. P. Catinella, L. Haas, and C. C. Hughes. "Cultures in Conflict: A Challenge to Faculty of Academic Health Centers." *Academic Medicine* 73 (August 1998): 871–875, http://www.ncbi. nim.gov (accessed on January 15, 2006).

Mangan, Katherine S. "Profits Are Small, But Many Academic Medical Centers Have Survived by Cutting Costs and Getting Tough with Insurers." *Chronicle of Higher Education* (January 31, 2003): 27.

Massey, Steve, and Mackenzie Carpenter. "Anatomy of a Bankruptcy: The Rise and Fall of Allegheny General Hospital." *Pittsburgh Post-Gazette* (January 17, 1999): C-1, C-4; 19: B-1; 20: C-1; 21: F-1, F-6, F-7; 22: D-1, D-6, D-7; 24: D-1.

Mayes, Rick, and Robert A. Berenson. *Medicare Prospective Payment and the Shaping of U.S. Health Care.* Baltimore: The Johns Hopkins University Press, 2006. http://www.press.jhu.edu (accessed on June 3, 2007).

McCullough, C. Hax, and Mary Brignano. *Pillar of Pittsburgh: The History of Mercy Hospital and the City It Serves.* Pittsburgh, 1990.

McGee, Marianne Kolbasuk. "Aggressive Treatment." *InformationWeek* (May 2, 2005), http://www.informationweek.com (accessed on May 23, 2005).

McGinley, Laurie. "Leading a Renaissance: Sicily Pegs Hope for Better Care, Economic Revival on Joint Transplant Venture with UPMC." *Wall Street Journal* (February 14, 2000): A-1. http://web.LexisNexis.com (accessed on December 5, 2006).

Merrill, James. *A Different Person: A Memoir.* New York: Knopf, 1993.

Minutes of the Senate Council Meeting of November 5, 1984, University Senate, University of Pittsburgh. Courtesy of The Senate of the University of Pittsburgh.

Moy, Ernest, MD, MPH; Paul F. Griner, MD; David R. Challoner, MD; and David R. Perry. "Distribution of Research Awards from the National Institutes of Health among Medical Schools." *New England Journal of Medicine* 342 (January 27, 2000): 250–255.

Myers, Eugene N., MD. "History of Our Department." Annual Report of University of Pittsburgh Department of Otolaryngology, 2004.

National Coalition on Health Care, "Health Insurance Cost," citing Poisal, J. A., et al., "Health Spending Projections Through 2016: Modest Changes Obscure Part D's Impact." *Health Affairs* 21 (February 2007: W242–253), http://www.nchc.org (accessed on April 15, 2008).

NIH Almanac – Appropriations. National Institutes of Health. http://www.nih.gov (accessed on May 6, 2007).

Otten, Alan L. "Jewish Healthcare Foundation." In *New Foundations in Health: Six Stories: A Report from the Milbank Memorial Fund* (May 1999). http://www.milbank.org (accessed on April 15, 2006).

Paull, Barbara I. *A Century of Medical Excellence: The History of the University of Pittsburgh School of Medicine.* Pittsburgh, 1986.

Pichot, Pierre. *A Century of Psychiatry.* F. Hoffmann–LaRoche & Co., Basel, Switzerland. Paris: Editions Roger DaCosta, 1983.

"Pittsburgh's BioMedical Centers of Excellence." Pittsburgh Regional Alliance with Sponsorship Provided by Jewish Healthcare Foundation. March 2001.

Poppick, Susie. "Former Med. School Dean Redlich, 93, Passes Away." *Yale Daily News* (January 21, 2004), http://www.yaledailynews.com (accessed on May 3, 2006).

Presbyterian-University Hospital Annual Reports.

Rand Health Research Highlights. "Effects of Medicare's Prospective Payment System on the Quality of Hospital Care." (1998). http:// www.rand.org (accessed on June 3, 2007).

Reston, Maeve. "President Gives Starzl Highest Prize." *Pittsburgh Post-Gazette* (February 14, 2006): A-16.

Robinet, Jane-Ellen. "A Crack in the Armor: DeStefano Leads Charge to Leave UPMC." *Pittsburgh Business Times* (March 27, 2000), http://pittsburgh.bizjournals.com

Romoff, Douglas. Videotaped interview with Jeffrey A. Romoff.

Romoff, Jeffrey A. "The Transformation of the Academic Medical Center." Speech, University of Pittsburgh (November 15, 1995).

———. "The Quality Equation: Leveraging Vision, Intelligence and Management for Successful Execution." Speech, UPMC Board Retreat (November 17, 2005).

———. "Creating New Growth Platforms: National and International Opportunities for UPMC." Speech, UPMC Board of Directors Executive Committee (August 8, 2006).

———. "A New Vision. A New Tomorrow: UPMC's Evolution as a Health Enterprise and Implications for Western Pennsylvania." Speech, UPMC Board Retreat (November 14, 2006).

Roth, Mark. "Infighting Behind Changes at Pitt?" *Pittsburgh Post-Gazette* (July 12, 1984): 4.

Scarf, Maggie. "In the 'Therapeutic Community,' Patients Are Doctors." *New York Times Magazine* (May 25, 1969), http://select.nytimes.com/gst/abstract.html (accessed on March 22, 2006).

Schachner, Marcia Kramer. "Western Psychiatric Institute and Clinic of the University of Pittsburgh: Its Years of Research, Teaching, and Service." Doctoral dissertation, University of Pittsburgh, Pittsburgh, 1984.

Simmons, Richard L., MD. "The Medawar Prize Acceptance Speech." *Transplantation* 79 (May 15, 2005): 1020–1021.

Snowbeck, Christopher. "Romoff Calls Highmark 'Ticket Scalpers.'" *Pittsburgh Post-Gazette* (May 4, 2002): A-7, http://infoweb.newsbank.com (accessed on July 7, 2008).

———. "UPMC, Pitt Cash in on Sale of High-Tech Medical Firm." *Pittsburgh Post-Gazette* (July 7, 2005), http://www.post-gazette.com (accessed on August 1, 2005).

———. "Banking on Research." *Pittsburgh Post-Gazette* (July 8, 2005): E-1.

———. "UPMC's Expertise for Sale Around the World." *Pittsburgh Post-Gazette* (October 22, 2006): D-1.

———. "UPMC, Mercy Merge – Venerable Catholic Hospital Joins Huge Health-Care System." *Pittsburgh Post-Gazette* (September 21, 2006): A-1, http://infoweb.newsbank.com (accessed on February 21, 2008).

Sonis, Meyer. *Skeletons in the Medical Closet: A Personal Story and Professional Report.* Loveladies, NJ: AuthorHouse, 2001.

———. *An Island Love Affair: A Family Memoir.* BookSurge Publishing, 2006.

Spice, Byron. "The Salk Vaccine: 50 Years Later." *Pittsburgh Post-Gazette* (April 3 and 4, 2005): A-5 and A-9; Record nos. 0504040304 and 0504040112.

Staresinic, Chuck. "The House That Hank Built." *Pitt Med* 4 (October 4, 2002): 12–15.

Starr, Paul. *The Social Transformation of American Medicine: The Rise of a Sovereign Profession and the Making of a Vast Industry.* New York: Basic Books, 1982.

DETRE THOMAS P
AM 76,480 A
31 January 1963
Thomas Detre
Brown Black 5'9" 158
17 May 24
Captain
USAR
05003743

Steele, Bruce. "Amidst Some Laughter, Detre Hall Is Dedicated." *University Times* 32 (May 25, 2000), http://www.pitt.edu (accessed on May 12, 2005).

———. "HealthAmerica and Blue Cross Skirmish Over Physician Deals." *University Times* 27, 11 (February 2, 1995), http://mac10.umc.pitt.edu (accessed June 3, 2006).

———. "Clinical Practice Plans Being Merged into Single Plan." *University Times* 29, 19 (May 29, 1997), http://www.umc.pitt.edu/utimes (accessed August 6, 2007).

———. "Administrators Discuss Unified Practice Plan." *University Times* 30, 13 (March 5, 1998), http://www.umc.pitt.edu/utimes (accessed August 6, 2007).

———. "Adler Says His Forced Resignation Is Not the Issue in Pitt Med School." *University Times* 30, 12 (February 19, 1998), http://www.umc.pitt.edu/utimes (accessed August 6, 2007).

Tipping, Emily J. "Appraising the Children's–UPMC Merger." *Physician's News Digest* (December 2001), http://physiciansnews.com (accessed on August 2, 2007).

Torpy, Janet M. "Health Care Insurance: The Basics." *Journal of the American Medical Association*, 297, 10 (March 14, 2007): 1154.

"Traveling the Road to Integration." UPMC Health System Retreat, Boston (1998).

Trends and Indicators in the Changing Health Care Marketplace. Section 1: Trends in Health Spending and Costs, Including Prescription Drugs. Kaiser Family Foundation. http://www.kff.org (accessed on April 25, 2007).

Tufts Managed Care Institute. "A Brief History of Managed Care." (1998).

UPMC. "Dipartimento Interaziendale per i Trapianti e Terapie ad Alta Specializzazione, Palermo, Italia: Economic Impact Study and Business Plan."

"UNOS Proposes to Refine Medical Urgency for Liver Transplant Candidates." UNOS News Bureau (August 10, 2000), http://www.unos.org.news (accessed December 9, 2006).

UPMC Health System. Statement on Financial Relationship with Istituto Mediterraneo per i Trapianti e Terapie ad Alta Specializzazione. Draft of April 16, 1999, quoting R. H. Hauboldt, *Cost Implications of Human Organ and Tissue Transplantations, an Update: 1996.* Research report published by Milliman & Robertson, Inc., 1997.

Van Der Werf, Martin. "Changing Economics of Health Care Are Devastating Academic Medical Centers." *Chronicle of Higher Education* (May 21, 1999): A-38.

Weeks, Brigitte. "How James Merrill Came of Age." *The New York Times* (December 12, 1993). *The New York Times on the Web.* http://www.nytimes.com (accessed on April 3, 2006).

Weimer, David L. "Public and Private Regulation of Organ Transplantation: Liver Allocation and the Final Rule." Robert M. La Follette School of Public Affairs. La Follette School Working Paper No. 2006-013. http://www.lafollette.wisc.edu (accessed on April 11, 2007).

Weiss, Rick. "Who Should Get Liver Transplants? As Demand Far Outpaces Donors, Federal Officials May Revamp Rules." *Washington Post* (December 9, 1996): A-01.

Western Psychiatric Institute and Clinic Annual Reports, 1971–1972 to 1979–1980.

Willis, Ellen. "Historical Analysis: Review of *Secrets of the Soul: A Social and Cultural History of Psychoanalysis* by Eli Zaretsky." *Dissent* 52 (Winter 2005): 113–116.

Wysocki, Bernard Jr. "At Pitt, Scientists Decode the Secret of Getting Grants." *Wall Street Journal Online* (June 28, 2004): Page One Feature, http://webreprints.djreprints.com/1041931195462.html (accessed on September 21, 2004).

Yablonski, Michael. "Mother Superior." *Pittsburgh Professional Magazine* (August 2007): 12–15, 70.

Archives

The Thomas Detre Collection, Papers of Thomas Detre, MD, Health Sciences Library System, University of Pittsburgh

University Archives, University of Pittsburgh

UPMC Archives

Additional

Various editions of *The New York Times, Pitt Magazine, Pitt Med, Pittsburgh Business Times, Physician's News Digest, Pittsburgh Catholic, Pittsburgh Post-Gazette, Pittsburgh Press, Pittsburgh Tribune-Review, University Times, The Wall Street Journal,* and the *Washington Post*

PHOTO CREDITS

All photographs courtesy of UPMC with the exception of those listed below.

Al Adams. Pages 192 (both), 203

Associate Photographers. Page 123 (top)

Courtesy of Henry T. Bahnson, MD (Source: *Pitt Med*), Page 59

Imre Berek. Page 18

Courtesy of George Board. Page 36

Pennsylvania Department, Carnegie Library of Pittsburgh. Flyleaf

Courtesy of J.W. Connolly. Page 82 (bottom)

Courtesy of Lila Decker. Page 46

Courtesy of Thomas Detre, MD. Pages 14, 16, 17, 20, 24 (top left), 231

The Archives of the Episcopal Diocese of Pittsburgh. Page 119 (bottom)

Detre Archive Collection, Falk Library of the Health Sciences, the University of Pittsburgh. Pages 21 (both), 22, 35, 57, 74, 109, 169, 170, 171, 175, 176 (bottom)

Special Collections, Falk Library of the Health Sciences, the University of Pittsburgh. Page 28 (bottom left & right)

Courtesy of Bernard Fisher, MD (Source: *Pitt Med*), Page 63

Joshua Franzos. Page 152

Copyright, Getty Images, Inc. All rights reserved. Page 17

Harry Giglio. Pages 131 (Children's Hospital), 158

Tom Gigliotti. Page 116

Scott Goldsmith. Pages 131 (Mercy Hospital), 163

Courtesy of George Huber. Pages 37, Concept Paper 90, 91

Reprinted with permission from the May 2, 2005 issue of *InformationWeek*. Copyright, 2005 United Business Media LLC. Page 198

Lynn Johnson. Pages 54 (top), 221

Jonas Photography. Page 32 (bottom)

Jim Judkis. Pages 71, 194

Courtesy of Rebecca Kaul. Page 38

Richard Kelly. Page 143

Karen Kuehn. Page 174 (left)

Hazel McManus. Page 188 (top)

Karen Meyers. Pages 125, 153, 235

Mizrahi, Inc. Pages 24–25 (book courtesy of WPIC Library), 213

Mark Perrott. Page 54 (bottom)

Piotris. Page 51

Copyright, *Pittsburgh Post-Gazette* Archives. All rights reserved. Reprinted with permission. Pages 41, 43, 61, 95, 103, 105, 112 (bottom), 126, 162, 168, 186 (bottom), 199, 211 (bottom), 216, 228, 233

Michael Ray. Page 127

Bill Redic. Page 89

Rieder Photography. Pages: cover, 2, 4, 8, 30–31, 52–53, 72–73, 96–97, 98 (bottom), 110–111, 120, 136–137, 146, 161, 164–165, 166 (top), 178, 180–181, 183, 184, 190–191, 204–205, 217 (both), 218–219

Courtesy of Jeffrey A. Romoff. Page 39 (both)

Standard Photo Group. Page 101

Studio Camera. Pages 173, 176 (top), 185

Archives Service Center, University of Pittsburgh. Pages 10–11, 12 (both), 28 (top), 29, 32 (top right), 44, 56, 58, 60 (bottom), 62 (bottom left), 174 (right)

Copyright, University of Pittsburgh/CIDDE. Jim Burke, pages 81 (top), 106; Bruce Steele, page 67

Courtesy of UPMC St. Margaret. Pages 119 (top), 121 (bottom)

Copyright, U.S. News & World Report LP. All rights reserved. Reprinted with permission. Page 187

Michaela Young. Page 157

ACKNOWLEDGMENTS

This book is a record of the memories, experiences, and points of view of remarkable individuals, and it would not have come about without the talent and effort of many people. First among them is George A. Huber, who initially proposed the idea of a history of UPMC and managed the project until his retirement from UPMC in 2007. George was an active partner in every interview and an insightful editor, and his intelligence, enthusiasm, creativity, good humor, and kindness are deeply appreciated. Sandra N. Danoff very knowledgably, sensitively, and adroitly picked up the reins and saw the book through to completion.

UPMC and the author appreciate those who graciously agreed to be interviewed and generously shared their time and memories.

Russell C. Brignano, PhD, meticulously transcribed the interviews, contributing immeasurably to the narrative. His perception and support, not to mention puns, are treasured.

Leslie Czechowski's archiving of Thomas Detre's papers made research even more of a pleasure, as did help from Barbara A. Epstein, MSLS; Deborah Lordi Silverman, MLS; other librarians of the Falk Library of the Health Sciences and the WPIC Library; University Archivist Marianne Kasica; Gilbert Pietrzak of the Pennsylvania Department, Carnegie Library of Pittsburgh; and Nancy J. Brown and Barbara DelRaso of the *University Times*. Leah Cirata, Eileen Johnson, Kathy Beltz, and Dawn A. Allan provided insight and administrative assistance. Always generous with their time, too, were Michele P. Jegasothy and Helen Horenzy.

Laurie R. Mizrahi, TJ Ladner, and Vincent R. Maffessanti of Mizrahi, Inc. created a uniquely handsome book. Additional photo research was provided by Laurie Mizrahi, Susan Corrigan, and Mary Brignano. Shirley Hamilton, Elizabeth Polen, Catherine Starr, and Sharon Tomasic were the proofreaders.

Every individual who has participated in UPMC's rapid ascent merits the thanks of western Pennsylvanians for improving the quality of life and livability of our region. Although this book focuses on administrative leaders, UPMC's success is also a product of the fine physicians, nurses, and all caregivers who expertly treat patients. Pittsburgh is a greater city because of them.

About the Author

Mary Brignano has authored and co-authored more than forty histories for prestigious foundations, cultural organizations, businesses, hospitals, and schools. Her clients have included the international law firm Reed Smith LLP, the Pittsburgh Civic Light Opera, the Pittsburgh Cultural Trust, UPMC Shadyside, UPMC St. Margaret, the Richard King Mellon Foundation, the Roy A. Hunt Foundation, the Historical Society of Western Pennsylvania Italian American Program, and Duquesne Light. Her publications have been recognized with numerous awards. Ms. Brignano is a graduate of the University of Wisconsin and holds an MA from the University of Pittsburgh.

Colophon

This book was designed by Laurie R. Mizrahi and TJ Ladner of Mizrahi, Inc., Pittsburgh, Pennsylvania, with the assistance of Vincent R. Maffessanti and Jason J. Dancisin. The text is set in Adobe Garamond Pro and HTF Knockout. The book was printed by Broudy Printing Inc., Pittsburgh, Pennsylvania, on Mohawk Superfine Ultrawhite Smooth, 80-lb text; the flyleaf on Neenah Eames Architecture Natural White, 50-lb text; and the endleaves on Smart Carnival Vertical White, 80-lb cover. The binding is by The Riverside Group, Rochester, New York.